Parenting a Child with Autism

A Modern Guide to Understand and Raise Your ASD Child to Success

Richard Bass

Table of Contents

If you would like to listen to this book for free, while you read along, please scan below.

Introduction

Autism can't define me, I define autism.

— Dr. Kerry Magro

Sir Isaac Newton, the man who discovered the laws of gravity and motion, will be remembered as the most influential scientist of all time—not as a high functioning autistic individual who had poor social skills and obsessive interests.

The great physicist, Albert Einstein, who developed the theory of relativity will be remembered as the "father of modern physics," and not how he only started speaking when he was three years old and displayed classic symptoms of autism throughout his life.

And what about Michaelangelo; the incredible artist whose work can be found on the ceiling of the Sistine Chapel? Although he was considered to have Asperger's disorder (which falls under the autism spectrum), he will be remembered for his incredible talent and contribution to the art and architecture communities.

Autistic people are differently abled. They experience the world with more richness and vibrancy. Colors are more vivid, sounds echo louder, and every sensation in their body is felt with a greater amount of sensitivity. As you can imagine, experiencing life in ultra HD can quickly become overwhelming—especially for a developing child with autism—which could result in stress, anxiety, and emotional outbursts.

However, as the great scientists and artists of our time have shown us, being autistic does not put children at a disadvantage. With the right psychological tools and techniques, children with autism can learn healthy ways to regulate their emotions, calm their bodies, and develop the confidence to live out their wildest dreams!

For many centuries, scientists and psychologists in the medical community didn't understand what autism was. It was only in the 20th century when a real investigation into the disorder began. Before then, doctors often misinterpreted the symptoms of autism spectrum disorder (ASD) as being signs of other psychological disorders.

For instance, children who had trouble focusing and maintaining eye contact were diagnosed with attention deficit hyperactivity disorder (ADHD), and others who had behavioral issues and trouble regulating their emotions were diagnosed with an antisocial personality disorder.

All the while, the real explanation for all these symptoms was ASD; a developmental disorder that causes several impairments in different parts of the brain. Since each child diagnosed with ASD showed different symptoms, doctors recognized that autism exists on a spectrum. For example, one child might have delayed speech development while another child might have a difficult time with social interactions—both of them still being on the autism spectrum.

Understanding this disorder hasn't been easy for doctors, as well as parents of children with ASD, since the jury is still out on what exactly causes autism. But one thing the medical community can agree on is that there is no cure for autism and there are currently no medications to treat it. The most effective interventions are early detection and diagnosis, as well as behavioral and educational therapies that can support the child's learning and development.

If you are reading this book, you may be particularly interested in learning more about ASD, and specifically how children with ASD think and experience the world. Perhaps you are an educator or parent who spends a lot of time caring for a child with autism. While there are many resources available online, you are open to discovering alternative interventions that can teach your child how to manage their emotions and age-appropriate communication skills.

Author and educator, Richard Bass, who holds a Bachelor's and Master's degree in Education and certifications in special education, has spent many years learning about children with special needs. Most of his time has been focused on understanding children's behaviors, disabilities, and mental health, and to date has published three books in these niches, namely: *A Beginner's Guide on Parenting Children with ADHD*, *Parenting Children with Oppositional Defiant Disorder*, and *Overcoming Anxiety and Depression in Teens*. Richard has also started a Facebook support group where further discussions about his books and the techniques covered in his books can take place.

As a member of numerous parenting, psychology, and educational online groups, Richard is passionate about helping parents get a better understanding of disorders and what can be done at home to see amazing differences in children's development. This book is no exception. Get ready to enter the mind and heart of your child with autism and learn how to provide them with the best start in life!

Chapter 1:

Understanding Autism

Through the Eyes of Your

Child

In this chapter, you will learn:

- What autism is and the recent developments in autism-related research.

- Common misconceptions about ASD and children with autism.

- The possible causes of autism and certain risk factors for expecting mothers.

What Is Autism Spectrum Disorder?

Autism Spectrum Disorder (ASD) is a developmental disorder that affects certain parts of the brain. As such, children with ASD may behave, interpret the world, communicate, and socialize differently than other children.

From their physical appearance, you cannot tell whether a child is on the spectrum or not. It is only when you compare the developmental milestones of neurotypical children to children with ASD that the signs and symptoms become more visible.

ASD can be diagnosed from three years old; although, early symptoms can appear from 12 months old. Since there isn't a known cure for ASD, this disorder persists throughout an individual's life, but symptoms can significantly improve when the right interventions are carried out.

Even though there is a lot of research coming out about ASD, it isn't a new disorder. Psychologists and scientists have known about ASD for more than 70 years. Nonetheless, how the medical community has understood autism has drastically changed over the centuries.

For example, in 1908, the word autism was used to describe schizophrenic children who were emotionally withdrawn and self-absorbed. In 1943, an American child psychiatrist named Leo Kanner described, in a paper, children who were incredibly intelligent but desired a lot of time alone. He called their condition "early infantile autism" (Sole-Smith, 2014).

A year later, a German scientist named Hans Asperger discovered a 'milder' form of autism in young boys, which he named Asperger's syndrome. The typical characteristics displayed by the boys were high intelligence, difficulty socializing with others, and obsessive interests.

In the early 1980s, infantile autism was added to the Diagnostic and Statistical Manual of Mental Disorders (DSM) and was seen as a separate condition from childhood schizophrenia. The name was later changed to "autism disorder" so it could include an expansive list of symptoms. A decade later, the U.S. federal government made autism a special education category and public schools began identifying children with signs of autism and providing a custom learning style.

In 2013, the DSM-5 combined all subcategories of autism under one diagnosis called autism spectrum disorder. This meant that Asperger's Syndrome would no longer be seen as a separate condition. Moreover, ASD could now be categorized by two main symptoms: impaired social communication/interaction and restricted or repetitive behaviors.

Misconceptions About ASD

Due to the lack of proper education about autism, there are many misconceptions out there about this condition. These misconceptions can be misleading and cause parents to fear having their children diagnosed with ASD. With more understanding, these misconceptions can be debunked and ensure that autistic children receive the support they deserve. Below are some of the common misconceptions you may hear or read about:

1. Autism Is a Disease

One common misconception is that autism is a disease. What makes this misconception harmful is that it implies that autism can be cured like any other disease, which we already know cannot happen. It also implies that autistic people have some sort of sickness, which once again is not true. Children with autism are not sick. They simply have a neuro-developmental disorder that causes communication impairments and other behavioral issues.

2. Vaccination Causes Autism

A study published in a journal in the 1990s argued that there was a link between autism and vaccines. The medical community found many loopholes in the study and it was later labeled as deceptive. Many years later, there are people who still believe vaccines cause autism although it hasn't been scientifically proven.

3. Autism Is Becoming an Epidemic

While the number of children diagnosed with autism has increased over the years, the condition is nowhere near becoming an epidemic. This misconception may be due to the fact that many parents and educators are now speaking out publicly about autism. The support for parents has also grown substantially, which makes it seem as though autism is more prevalent nowadays than it was many decades ago.

4. All Autistic People Have a Savant Skill

Savant syndrome is a condition where an individual with mental impairments demonstrates exceptional abilities in certain areas. Savant syndrome has been historically linked to developmental conditions like ASD and has made society believe that every autistic person has a savant skill. While it is true that some autistic people are incredibly gifted (1 in 10 autistic people to be specific), not every autistic person will have an exceptional ability.

5. Autistic People Don't Feel Emotion

It is a myth that autistic people cannot feel emotion, or cannot express their full range of emotions. Like any other human being, an autistic individual is capable of feeling a wide range of emotions. However, they may struggle to communicate or regulate their emotions, which makes them come across as withdrawn or disinterested. There are also cases, specifically with children with autism, where they experience emotional flooding. They become overwhelmed when their strong emotions take over, which can lead to stress, emotional outbursts, and anxiety.

The Autism Spectrum Explained

If you have a child living with autism, a doctor may diagnose them with a type of autism. Since autism exists on a spectrum, there are five types of autism, each having their own symptoms and challenges. Understanding which type of autism your child has will ensure you provide the best care possible. Here are the five types of autism and a list of common symptoms each of them come with:

1. Asperger's Syndrome

Asperger's syndrome was the term used to describe a condition where a child had above average intelligence and difficulty with social interactions. After 2013, the condition was reclassified as "Level 1 autism spectrum disorder," however, many in the autism community continue to refer to the condition as Asperger's Syndrome. In general, a child with level 1 autism spectrum disorder will display the following symptoms:

- Inflexible and repetitive behavior and thought

- Preference for specific kinds of activities

- Difficulty understanding social cues, such as another person's body language or facial expressions

- Obsessive habits that can at times interfere with other daily activities

- Becoming irritable with unexpected changes to routine

2. Rett Syndrome

Rett syndrome is typically noticeable during infancy. It is more likely to affect girls; it is considered rare for boys to be diagnosed with Rett syndrome. This condition causes significant challenges for young children that affect every aspect of their lives. Some of the typical symptoms of Rett syndrome include:

- Loss of mobility or lack of coordination.

- Reduced muscle tone.

- Challenges with speech.

- Reduced functionality in hands or involuntary hand movements.

- Difficulty breathing and sleeping (this can lead to sleeping disorders).

- Abnormal curvature of the spine.

3. Childhood Disintegrative Disorder

Childhood Disintegrative Disorder (CDD), also known as Heller's syndrome, is a developmental disorder characterized by delayed speech, motor skills, and social functioning. A child may reach all of their developmental milestones, up until the age of three (or at any age before 10) when they hit a developmental regression. Parents can be caught off guard by this developmental gap since their child showed typical growth, up to the point when the regression started. The regression can occur at once or gradually, and a child may lose the following skills or abilities:

- Control of bowel and bladder movements

- Learned language and vocabulary

- Social skills and adaptive behaviors

- Playing abilities

4. Kanner's Syndrome

American Psychiatrist Leo Kanner discovered Kanner's syndrome, which he originally called infantile autism. Kanner's syndrome is a classic autism disorder characterized by the following symptoms:

- Difficulty forming emotional attachments to others

- Obsession with handling different objects

- Uncontrollable speech

- Learning problems in certain areas

5. Pervasive Developmental Disorder—Not Otherwise Specified

Pervasive Developmental Disorder—Not Otherwise Specified (PDD-NOS) is a 'milder' type of autism that causes difficulties in social and language development. A child with PDD-NOS has some, but not all symptoms of autism. Therefore, you can identify this condition by examining which developmental delays or impairments your child is experiencing. Doctors will often diagnose a child with PDD-NOS when they do not fulfill the criteria for other classifications of autism. Common symptoms of PDD-NOS can include:

- Communication problems

- Unusual social behavior

- Underdeveloped speech

- Repetitive and persistent behaviors

- High sensitivity to smell, sounds, light, food, and physical touch

Risk Factors Behind Autism

Up until now, scientists have not been able to determine the cause of ASD. Understandably, this can be extremely frustrating for parents. However, recent studies point to a number of factors that can make growing fetuses or small children more vulnerable to developing this disorder than other children. Below are a few risk factors to consider:

1. Brain and Body Changes

An article published by The Korean Society for Brain and Neural Sciences investigated brain scans of people with autism and those of typical people. The researchers found that during early childhood, the brains of children with autism develop faster than usual (Ha et al., 2015). This rapid brain growth can explain the mental acuity that is common in children with autism. There is also research that suggests bacterial infections contracted during pregnancy can increase the risk of a growing fetus developing ASD, however, a bacterial infection doesn't play a strong role in the development of autism.

2. Family History and Genetics

There is evidence showing how autism can be passed down through family lineage. Children born in families with a history of autism are more vulnerable to developing autism. Even if both parents are not autistic, they could be carriers of the gene that causes autism. Scientists are still investigating how the autism gene is passed down through family lineage, and what causes some children to be at a higher risk of developing autism than others. When there is no family history of autism, parents who have their children later in life can put their little ones at a higher risk of developing autism. Other pregnancy complications, such as premature birth, can also be a contributing factor.

3. Environment

Apart from brain, body, and genetic factors, autism can also be caused by environmental factors, such as exposure to toxic chemicals, air pollutants, medication, and viral infections. What's even more surprising, those who are already predisposed to the disorder are at an even higher risk of developing autism due to these environmental factors.

4. Other Disorders

Children who have been diagnosed with other medical conditions are vulnerable to developing autism. Such medical conditions include fragile X syndrome (a disorder that causes mental problems), tuberous sclerosis (a benign tumor that develops in the brain), or Rett syndrome.

What It's Really Like for a Child With Autism

There isn't a lot of information in the media about what an autistic life actually looks like. As a result, people often turn to stereotypes to understand what autistic individuals go through.

However, these stereotypes can be damaging because they are not true.

To understand how a child with autism sees the world, imagine that you have arrived in a foreign non-English speaking country and attempt to find your way without a translator. You would feel frustrated knowing that everybody around you can communicate with each other effortlessly, but there are certain social cues and rules you need to learn. This is how a child with autism experiences the world. On good days, they can feel puzzled and on bad days, they can feel extremely overwhelmed.

One of the ways children with autism self-soothe is by practicing what is known as stimming. This is a repetitive motion or noise they make that might look unusual. Other children with autism will flap their arms, spin around, or any other motion or repetitive behavior that can help them "zone out" for a while and calm their nervous system.

Unfortunately, stimming is often frowned upon. A parent who isn't aware of their child's autism might interpret this self-soothing technique as fidgeting or making unnecessary noise. They might reprimand their child for stimming, causing them to learn that regulating their body in this manner is inappropriate. Hiding stimming leads to another common behavior known as masking.

Some children mask better than others, although the message they grow up learning is that being different from neurotypical children is not acceptable. The reality is that masking is stressful since it requires a child with autism to hide natural inclinations and adopt behaviors that don't feel normal. Masking may hide classic autistic symptoms, but it won't cure the disorder. All it does is make the child feel ashamed of displaying who they truly are.

A common stereotype about children with autism is that they lack empathy. From a child with autism's perspective, this isn't true. Like any other human being, a child with autism has the capacity to feel a wide range of emotions. The difference between them and typical children is they struggle to express their emotions, or when they eventually do express their emotions, they may find it difficult to regulate them.

Emotional regulation skills are an indispensable tool for children with autism because they teach them how to control what they are feeling and express their emotions in a healthy way. Throughout the day, a child with autism is bursting with emotions internally due to their sensitivity to stimuli in their surroundings. When they express these emotions, they come out raw and unfiltered. Sadness, for example, can be expressed as extreme and inconsolable sorrow, while happiness can be expressed with loud squealing and jumping up and down. Once again, this kind of expression can be considered socially inappropriate, which might cause a child with autism to mask their emotions.

Furthermore, children with autism process information differently. This means that they use different mental strategies to interpret the world around them. Here are a few mental processes that are commonly used by children with autism:

1. Detail-Oriented Approach to Learning

When neurotypical children learn information, they may start by understanding the concept first, then breaking it down into several different components. For example, they might learn that a school bus is a mode of transportation that takes them to school. Thereafter, they would unpack the other components of a school bus, such as its size, speed, color, and so forth.

A child with autism learns concepts by understanding the various components it consists of, rather than looking at them from an abstract, top-down approach. When learning about a school bus, they might memorize the size, color, and intricate details of a bus and record that as being a school bus. Tomorrow, when they see another school bus with different characteristics, they won't recognize it as a school bus unless they are told. They might add these new characteristics into their "school bus" category, but if they see a third school bus with different characteristics, they might not be able to recognize it as a school bus.

This detail-oriented approach to learning also applies when a child with autism is taught a skill. For example, they can be taught how to share toys at home with their younger siblings, but that doesn't mean they will remember to share their toys at school or in any other setting. Therefore the best way to reinforce a skill with a child with autism is to focus on repetition and exposure to as many variables as possible to build on a concept.

2. Interpret Information Literally

When it comes to communication, a child with autism will interpret what you say literally and won't be able to pick up on sarcasm, figurative speech, and other indirect social, language, or body cues. For example, if you say, "It's raining cats and dogs," your child with autism might look outside of the window expecting to see cats and dogs falling from the sky.

Taking things literally can make it hard for your child to understand phrases that are supposed to be serious or humorous. It might also cause your child to say things that come off as rude because they don't realize that being completely truthful isn't always polite. For example, commenting on a meal tasting awful can hurt their mother's feelings, even though it wasn't the child's intention to do so.

3. Difficulty Learning Sequences

Have you noticed that your child with autism can be forgetful when given instructions at times? This isn't due to a lack of concentration, but rather their difficulty in learning sequences. For example, if you tell a child with autism to go upstairs to the bathroom, pick up the laundry basket, come back down to the laundry room, and drop the basket off, they might only remember the first two instructions and forget what to do next. The same applies when they are given a list of chores, directions, or homework instructions.

When teaching your child sequencing, avoid lecturing information. Instead, write down the steps they need to take on a piece of paper or use visual representations like pictures, diagrams, or color-coded information to make following steps easier.

Exercise: Step Into Your Child's Shoes

Imagine if you spent a day in your child with autism's world. How would you interpret the stimuli around you? How would you respond to casual conversations? Below is a table consisting of typical behavior displayed by children with ASD. Next to each scenario, write down your perspective as a parent, then in the next column, write down your child's perspective.

Scenario	Parent's Perspective	Child's Perspective
eg. Meltdown in a supermarket.	"My child is causing trouble and throwing a tantrum."	"The bright LED lights and loud public music is making me anxious. I want to go home!"
Taking a long time to complete homework.		
Seeming disinterested when guests arrive at home.		
Asking a lot of questions.		
Getting upset when routines are changed.		

Key Takeaways

ASD is a developmental disorder that affects different parts of the brain, which causes children to learn, behave, and communicate differently than neurotypical children. Since ASD is not a disease, there is no cure or medication to treat it. However, learning more about the disorder, its risk factors, and how autistic children view the world can help parents provide their children with the appropriate support and nurturing they deserve.

Now that you have a better understanding of what autism is—and isn't—it's time to take a closer look at the signs and symptoms for recognizing ASD.

Chapter 2:

Early Signs of ASD and Those

All-Important First Steps

In this chapter you will learn:

- The common signs and symptoms of ASD.

- Who can diagnose ASD and the process involved in getting a diagnosis.

Signs and Symptoms of ASD

Dr. Stephen Shore, a special education professor at Adelphi University, once said "If you've met one person with autism, you've met one person with autism" (Egber, 2021). By saying this, he meant that every person diagnosed with autism is unique in their own right. This is true since the symptoms of autism vary from one child with autism to another and what one child may find challenging, another may find simple.

Doctors can diagnose ASD from as early as three years old, although early signs may start to appear from 12 months onward. Two of the common signs of autism include communication problems and difficulty connecting with others socially. Other common symptoms are:

- Delayed speech

- Little to no eye contact

- Dependency on structure and routine

- Becoming irritable by minor lifestyle changes

- Sensitivity to smell, light, sounds, and physical touch

- Obsession with specific interests and objects

- Repetitive behaviors, such as flapping hands or spinning around

Due to the fact that ASD is a developmental disorder, children with this condition will not develop certain abilities as expected. For example, if a newborn does not reach their developmental milestones by the age of one, then it may be time to visit a specialist to test for autism or other developmental conditions. With that said, parents shouldn't be quick to panic when their little ones take longer to reach certain milestones.

Here are some of the early signs that your infant may have ASD:

- No babbling by the four-month mark

- No smiling by the five-month mark

- No laughing by the six-month mark

- No interest in games like peek-a-boo by the eight-month mark

- Doesn't respond to their name by the twelve-month mark

- Not looking at objects pointed out by other people by the twelve-month mark

- Becoming easily frightened by loud noises

- Preferring to play alone for long periods of time

Between the ages of one and two, your toddler may show other symptoms of ASD, such as:

- Not being able to say 'mama' or 'dada,' or being able to repeat phrases

- Repeating words and sounds they are comfortable with over and over again

- Lacking interest being around other children

- Not imitating other people's facial expressions

The signs and symptoms of autism are normally evident by the age of three. A few ASD behaviors may become more apparent, such as:

- Expressing a limited range of emotions sadness, restlessness, and excitement, or not expressing emotions at all

- Difficulty reacting to other people's emotions

- Seeming unattached from parents

- Lack of interest in participating in social games

- Preferring to play with one particular object or toy

- Having frequent tantrums and meltdowns

In more critical cases, symptoms of ASD can impact your child's functioning range. Some of the severe symptoms to look out for include:

- Not speaking at all

- Becoming extremely upset with changes in daily routine

- Displaying challenging behavior, such as being physically aggressive or banging head against a wall

- Requires assistance with daily tasks, such as bathing, using the toilet, and dressing

- Developing rigid preferences for certain objects, foods, people, or clothes

Studies indicate that between 25—50 percent of children living with ASD do not develop verbal communication skills. Moreover, after the age of five, it is rare for a non-speaking child with autism to develop verbal communication skills. This means that it is normal for most children with autism to become non-speaking teens and adults.

What Does Developmental Milestones Mean?

As a child grows, they cross several growth milestones, which ensure they are progressing appropriately. Tracking your child's milestones can help you keep track of their development and identify developmental delays early on.

You can think of developmental milestones as a checklist that measures the progress of an average child. The timing of each milestone can vary, however, if milestones aren't reached within the expected range, it can raise concerns.

There are different types of developmental milestones that you or your child's pediatrician can look out for, which may include:

- **Physical milestones:** Examples of physical milestones are fine motor and large motor skills, such as being able to pick up a spoon (fine motor skill) or crawl or walk (large motor skill). In general, it can take the average child up to 18 months before they start walking (Burch, 2022).

- **Cognitive milestones:** These milestones are focused on a child's ability to think, learn, and solve problems. An example of a cognitive milestone for an infant would be learning to recognize and imitate different facial expressions, and for a toddler, practicing reciting the alphabet.

- **Social and emotional milestones:** These milestones are concerned with a child's ability to identify and understand their own emotions, as well as other people's emotions. Examples of key milestones in this category include being able to interact and play with other children, expressing emotion through various facial expressions, reacting to another person's display of emotion, and self-soothing.

- **Communication milestones:** Examples of communication milestones are verbal and nonverbal communication skills. Verbal skills in small children may include learning to make cooing sounds, trying to find the person calling out their name, and learning to say certain words and phrases. Nonverbal skills may include shaking the head to express disagreement or making facial expressions like smiling or frowning.

The following developmental milestones are a combination of the different types of milestones and show examples of what an average child is able to display at various stages in their development (remember that each child is unique and may reach a milestone earlier or later than their peers):

9 Month Milestones
- Smiles or laughs while engaging in interactive games
- Babbles or tries to imitate normal speech with noises

- Notices when objects have dropped and tries to find them

- Makes a number of facial expressions

- Gets themselves in a sitting position without support

12 Month Milestones

- Enjoys playing social games with caregivers

- Makes gestures like waving goodbye or shaking their head in disapproval

- Has the ability to recognize their parents and call them by their name

- Plays with different objects and tries to stack or combine them

- Pulls themselves up so they can stand and balances on furniture to walk

18 Month Milestones

- Imitates caregiver's actions while playing with toys

- Has three or more frequently used words or phrases besides 'mama' and 'dada'

- Follows single instructions without requiring gestures for assistance

- Points to objects to show caregiver something of interest

- Holds food and feeds themselves with their fingers

- Climbs on and off low furniture without assistance

24 Month Milestones

- Reacts when someone near them cries or looks upset

- Plays with a range of toys at the same time, such as pushing a wheelbarrow with several stuffed animals inside

- Combines at least two words to convey simple messages to caregiver

- Uses a range of gestures, besides pointing and waving hands, such as shrugging shoulders as a way of showing they don't know the answer

- Walks up a few stairs with or without assistance

36 Month Milestones

- Notices other children playing and walks toward them to join

- Responds to questions with simple but coherent sentences

- Asks a range of who, what, where, why, and how questions

- Dresses themselves in the morning

The Diagnostic Process

The DSM consists of various classifications of psychiatric disorders to help medical professionals in the process of diagnosing patients. Medical professionals may refer to different editions of the manual to look for diagnostic codes for specific disorders. In the latest edition, DSM-5, the manual updated the criteria for diagnosing autism and other related disorders. For instance, disorders like Asperger's syndrome and PDD-NOS, which used to be diagnosed separately, are now under the umbrella category called ASD.

When diagnosing ASD, doctors must ensure that children meet three criteria that have to do with deficits in social interactions and communication. These criteria should not be due to developmental delays since these are natural and aren't signs of autism. The three criteria include:

- Difficulty in maintaining back and forth conversations, sharing interests with others, and expressing or understanding emotions

- Difficulty recognizing nonverbal communication like facial expressions or gestures used for communication, which are useful in social interactions

- Difficulty building and maintaining close relationships with people who aren't their caregivers or part of their immediate family

The DSM-5 criteria for ASD diagnosis also requires children to display at least two out of the four restricted and repetitive behaviors below:

- Repetitive speech or questioning, repetitive motor movements, repetitive words or phrases, abnormal phrases, and repetitive use of objects

- Rigid adherence to rules and routines, ritualized patterns of communication, and extreme resistance to change

- Displaying intense focus on specific interests and obsessions with certain topics, objects, or activities

- Increased or decreased reactivity to sensory information within their surroundings, such as having disdain for certain smells or food textures or not reacting to physical pain

Along with the criteria for diagnosing ASD, the DSM-5 has included a severity rating, which classifies children under three levels of severity for the disorder. The three levels are as follows:

Level 1: Requiring Support

Children under this level of severity may have difficulty interacting with others. Some of the communication problems they might face include:

- Unusual or unsuccessful responses to social interactions

- Decreased interest in social interactions

- Challenges maintaining a back and forth conversation

- Difficulty making friends

They may also experience repetitive behaviors that get in the way of their daily functioning. For instance, once they are focused on a really interesting activity, they may have difficulty switching to another one.

Level 2: Requiring Substantial Support

Children under this level of severity tend to experience delays in verbal and nonverbal communication. They may seem disinterested in playing with other children or responding to social cues. Some of the communication problems they might face include:

- Noticeable difficulties with verbal or nonverbal communication skills

- Limited response to social interactions with others

- Limited initiation of social interactions with others

They may also display inflexible behavior and become upset when they discover changes to their routine.

Level 3: Requiring Very Substantial Support

Children under this level of severity may experience severe impairments to their daily functioning. Due to their condition, they may have limited to no response to social interactions and may be limited in verbal communication skills. They can also have a hard time coping with change and find the process of switching focus or action distressing.

It is worth mentioning that many doctors prefer to diagnose children with autism based on the DSM-5 criteria for ASD, rather than relying on these three severity levels. Screening for autism can take place at your child's 18-month or 24-month check-ups. If you have any concerns about your child's developmental milestones, you can also complete an online screener and discuss the results with your physician. Please note that you don't need to wait to get an autism diagnosis before addressing problems related to your child's developmental delays. You can find a local and free early intervention program or contact your district's Special Education office.

Lastly, your child can only be diagnosed with ASD by a registered medical professional—not their school teacher or concerned family members. Furthermore, since autism is more than a personality disorder, it requires a lot of testing and evaluation before a diagnosis can be given. The medical doctors who are qualified to give your child a diagnosis are developmental pediatricians, child psychologists, child psychiatrists, and pediatric neurologists. You can also opt to get a second opinion from qualified child therapists who may know more about autism than general doctors. Examples of these specialized therapists are speech therapists, occupational therapists, social workers, and physical therapists.

Exercise: Preparing for Diagnosis

Based on the signs and symptoms of ASD, as well as the typical developmental milestones, think about your own child's development and behavior. Create three lists; one for milestones or typical behavior that is not present, the second for concerns you might have, and another for definite signs and symptoms of autism that already appear. Take these three lists with you when you visit your child's doctor for their next check-up. They will help you and the doctor during the diagnosis stage.

Key Takeaways

Parents can feel confused and upset when their children are not growing or learning as quickly as other kids. However, delayed development is more common than one might think. The only time parents should be concerned is when their children do not reach milestones within the expected stages. Getting a diagnosis from a medical specialist can be what puts both parents and children at ease, as they finally get to learn whether their little ones have a developmental disorder, like ASD, or not. The diagnostic process must be conducted by a licensed doctor who is familiar with the DSM-5 criteria. But this doesn't mean parents should underestimate the feedback from their children's teachers, especially when they are older.

The stress and strain of taking care of a child with ASD do not start and end with getting a diagnosis. There are also a number of different disorders and health conditions that may present with ASD. Because the signs are so varied, it is also very common for a parent to misread the symptoms. The following chapter will help clear this up.

Chapter 3:

ASD and Related Health

Concerns

In this chapter you will learn:

- Other significant health conditions that might be present with ASD.

- The difference between ASD and ADHD, and other related disorders.

What Conditions Are Associated With ASD?

Living with autism causes mental, emotional, and physical changes for your child. Even before receiving a diagnosis, you may notice that your child is experiencing anxiety, digestive issues, or trouble sleeping. It is very rare for ASD to exist alone. Typically, it will trigger other secondary medical conditions or issues. Part of your intervention program as a parent should involve ways of not only reducing ASD-related symptoms, but improving your child's overall mental, emotional, and physical well-being.

Here are some of the conditions your child may experience along with ASD:

1. Gastrointestinal Disorders

It has been found that gastrointestinal disorders are eight times more common in children with autism than in neurotypical children. Some of the common GI issues experienced include chronic constipation, bowel inflammation, abdominal pain, and gastroesophageal reflux.

2. Epilepsy

Epilepsy, also known as a seizure disorder, can affect as much as a third of autistic people, including children. Some of the early signs of epilepsy include constantly feeling sleepy, interrupted sleep, and unexplained mood changes. Although when your child experiences staring spells, involuntary movements, and severe headaches, it is time to visit a specialist doctor, such as a neurologist.

3. Eating Problems

Eating problems are extremely common among children with autism. The types of issues can range from having restricted food habits to being averse to certain flavors or textures. Most food problems occur as a result of a child with autism's hypersensitivity or the desire to maintain a rigid and non-experimental diet. Speaking to a therapist or nutritionist about your child's food problems can help to improve eating behaviors.

4. Interrupted Sleep

Many children living with autism experience chronic sleep problems. This is because they struggle to fall asleep or have uninterrupted sleep during the night. Since they are not able to get a good night's rest, they wake up feeling tired and cranky. When sleep problems aren't addressed, they can affect your child's daily functioning and worsen their behavioral challenges.

5. ADHD

Attention deficit and hyperactivity disorder (ADHD) affects about six to seven percent of the population. However, the same condition affects between 30—60 percent of people with autism. ADHD is characterized by regular patterns of inattention, forgetfulness, challenging time management, and impulsivity that interferes with daily routine. The symptoms of ADHD can overlap with the symptoms of ASD, however, more will be said about this in the following chapter.

6. Anxiety

Some of the symptoms of autism include experiencing difficulty starting conversations, expressing emotions, and participating in social interactions. These symptoms can cause the child to experience social anxiety around other people. They might also feel anxious when they feel strong emotions like anger and cannot find a healthy way to express it. Anxiety can also be triggered by heart palpitations, stomach cramps, headaches, or any other physical sensation that they are not familiar with.

7. Depression

The rates of depression among people with autism tend to rise with age and cognitive development. Some ASD-related communication behaviors like withdrawing from others or seeming disinterested can hide signs of depression. However, parents can look out for a few red flags, such as losing interest in activities that were once enjoyable, chronic sadness, irritability, and worsening hygiene habits. If you suspect that your child may be depressed, consult a mental health specialist for a professional evaluation.

8. OCD

Obsessive compulsive disorder (OCD) is more commonly seen in teens and adults with autism. In young children, it can be difficult to distinguish between repetitive behaviors and specific obsessions, and a case of OCD. To get an accurate diagnosis of OCD, consult a mental health specialist.

9. Schizophrenia

ASD and schizophrenia are similar in that both cause children to experience difficulty processing language and understanding how others think and feel. However, the difference is that schizophrenia can cause hallucinations. Classic symptoms of schizophrenia are more noticeable during early adulthood.

10. Bipolar Disorder

Bipolar disorder is a mental condition that causes alternations between high energy emotional states and low energy emotional states. It is important to observe your child's behaviors and recognize when symptoms appear and how long they have appeared. This is because what comes across as bipolar symptoms could be part of your child's autism. When your child has been diagnosed with bipolar disorder, be mindful of the type of medication they are given. Some bipolar medication can worsen symptoms of autism, such as the ability to recognize and express emotion. A child psychiatrist can advise you on the best treatment options for your child.

The Difference Between ASD and ADHD

A kindergarten school teacher reported that a child was misbehaving in class. The parents of the child were already familiar with their son's hyperactive behavior. They believed hyperactivity was a sign of ADHD since it has been a trend for young children to be diagnosed with ADHD. However, this was a misdiagnosis because the child was autistic. This meant that for six months, the child was given ADHD medication, rather than seeking treatment for ASD.

Many parents often confuse signs of ASD with signs of ADHD. This happens because the two conditions share a range of symptoms, such as difficulty paying attention, being constantly on the move, having frequent meltdowns, and not being able to pick up on social cues.

ASD and ADHD are similar because they are both developmental disorders that affect different parts of the brain. Both tend to range in severity, but ASD exists on a spectrum whereas ADHD doesn't. It's also worth noting that the common signs of ASD are challenges with social interactions and communication skills, while common signs of ADHD are challenges with concentration and managing impulses.

In the previous chapter, we discussed the common signs and symptoms of ASD, which included factors like delayed speech, repetitive behaviors, obsessive interests, and communication difficulties. These are different from the common signs and symptoms of ADHD which include:

- Getting easily distracted or daydreaming

- Trouble following instructions

- Difficulty completing tasks

- Being impatient

- Acting without thinking about the consequences

The social and emotional impact of these conditions are also different. For instance, since a child with ASD may struggle to relate with others, they may find it difficult to make friends. This may cause them to prefer playing alone or being around familiar faces, rather than broadening their social circle. A child with ADHD, on the other hand, finds it difficult to follow socially acceptable norms like sitting still, keeping quiet, or enduring test situations at school. As a result, they may be labeled as troublesome or disruptive, and this negative feedback could affect how they perceive themselves and their condition.

Fortunately, the same type of doctors can diagnose both ASD and ADHD, but the treatment plan will differ. A child with ASD is more likely to be put on an early intervention program or introduced to several types of therapies like cognitive behavioral therapy (CBT), social skills training therapies, or speech therapy. In contrast, a child with ADHD may be prescribed ADHD medication, as well as anxiety medication, and they might also benefit from CBT and learning organizational and time management skills.

Other Commonly Confused Conditions

Besides ADHD, there are other conditions commonly confused with ASD. They share similar symptoms, but also consist of striking differences. Here are six to consider:

1. Williams Syndrome

Williams syndrome is a genetic disorder affecting one out of 10,000 people. It is caused by missing DNA material on chromosome 7 in humans. Some of the symptoms of Williams syndrome look identical to symptoms of autism. These include speech and developmental delays, challenges with gross motor skills, sensitivity to sound, and rigid food preferences. However, what makes this condition different from autism is the fact that it also causes cardiovascular abnormalities, increased calcium levels, and high blood pressure. Sufferers may also display pixie-like facial features, such as oval ears, almond-shaped eyes, narrow faces, and small chins.

2. Fragile X

Another genetic disorder similar to ASD is Fragile X syndrome. It affects males more than females and can cause cognitive impairments. It has been found that about 20% of people with Fragile X syndrome display autistic-type symptoms, such as hand flapping, unusual gestures, and little eye contact. Some people with this condition have certain facial features like a long face, poor muscle tone, and flat feet; however, this isn't the case with all sufferers. Blood tests are required as part of the diagnostic process and mild medication can treat behavioral issues.

3. Landau-Kleffner Syndrome

Landau-Kleffner syndrome is a form of epilepsy that causes speech loss. It typically develops in children between the ages of three and seven and is twice as common in males than females. Children with this condition may or may not be autistic. In their early years, they may reach their developmental milestones, but as they grow older, their speaking and language skills may start to regress—until they lose their ability to speak and understand speech. Autism-like symptoms seen in those with this condition include tolerance to pain, insistence on rigid routines, and little eye contact.

4. Prader-Willi Syndrome

Prader-Willi Syndrome is another condition associated with autism. It carries classic autism symptoms, such as obsession with food (which can lead to impulsive eating), temper tantrums, and delays in speech and language. However, some unique symptoms include poor muscle tone, underdeveloped sexual characteristics, and a compact body build. The most effective intervention for Prader-Willi syndrome is behavior therapy.

5. Angelman Syndrome

Angelman Syndrome is a genetic disorder that tends to appear within a child's first year. It is caused by missing DNA material on chromosome 15, which affects the functioning of the child's nervous system. Autism-type symptoms include speech impairments, hand flapping, and learning difficulties. Other typical symptoms include hyperactivity, epilepsy, and difficulty sleeping.

6. Tardive Dyskinesia

Tardive Dyskinesia causes involuntary movements like excessive blinking, foot-tapping, or head nodding. To calm the symptoms of this condition, neuroleptic medications are recommended. When medication is not taken, the symptoms often become worse. The repetitive behaviors displayed by those with tardive dyskinesia can be confused with classic repetitive behaviors related to autism. However, the difference is that tardive dyskinesia movements are less complex and occur involuntarily.

Even though these six conditions can display ASD-type symptoms, it is important to seek a specific diagnosis and special treatment from a qualified medical professional.

Chapter Takeaways

Since ASD is a broad umbrella term, it consists of many sub-conditions that have similar symptoms. Moreover, ASD can be confused with other neurodevelopmental disorders like ADHD, or personality disorders like anxiety or bipolar disorder. It is advised to consult a doctor to evaluate your child's health condition and identify any underlying medical conditions besides ASD.

These chapters have focused on what ASD looks like, what it isn't, and the common signs to help clarify the condition. Even though you will need to wait for an official diagnosis to receive specialized help, there are simple interventions you can do at home to help your child with autism. The next chapter starts with helping your child manage their emotions.

Chapter 4:

Managing Big Feelings in

Little People

In this chapter you will learn:

- How to help your child recognize and regulate their emotions.

The Emotions of a Child With Autism

Imagine going to an art gallery and looking at the same piece of artwork as the crowd. While they all agree on seeing something quite specific, you see the opposite. No matter what angle you look at it from, you can't see what they see. Eventually, you are going to feel frustrated, annoyed, and even enraged. This is how a child with autism feels on a regular basis, except they are not viewing art, but people's faces.

Humans have six primary emotions: surprise, happiness, anger, sadness, disgust, and fear. However, these primary emotions can bring about secondary emotions, which are more complex in nature. These include emotions like trust, guilt, envy, shame, or contempt. From birth, newborn babies start to learn how to identify and express primary and secondary emotions, and usually by two months old, babies can laugh or react in fear.

By 12 months, children are able to read facial expressions and react to how you are feeling. The older they get, the better they become at understanding feelings and using words to express their feelings or emotions they recognize in others. By the time a child reaches adulthood, they are more skilled at expressing and regulating their emotions, as well as showing empathy for others.

Since we already understand that ASD is a developmental disorder, children with autism may experience difficulty expressing their emotions. Similar to non-autistic babies, newborn autistic babies are able to recognize emotions, however, they are not as proficient at developing emotional responses. Some of the emotions that are commonly recognized by children with autism are happiness and sadness. They may have a hard time recognizing fear, anger, or disgust.

The challenge with recognizing certain emotions may continue into adulthood.

School-aged children with autism may struggle to put their feelings into words, such as communicating how they are feeling. Children within the same age group with more severe autism may show less emotional expression than school-aged neurotypical children. This could make it seem as though children with severe autism don't feel anything, however, that isn't the case. They can feel and recognize emotion but have trouble responding emotionally.

Are Children With Autism Empathetic?

A common myth about children with autism is that they do not have the capacity to show empathy. This myth stems from the inability of some children with autism to express emotions, which causes them to come across as aloof or disinterested in social interactions. However, this type of behavior can be a sign of a condition that affects up to 50 percent of autistic people, called alexithymia.

Alexithymia is simply defined as the inability to describe feelings. A child with alexithymia may find it challenging to process and communicate their emotions. Although this doesn't mean they have fewer emotions than other children. There is even research that suggests that it is due to alexithymia, not autism symptoms, that makes it harder for children to understand another person's emotional experience (Shah et al., 2016).

An older child with autism with alexithymia will usually tell when they are experiencing a strong emotion, but they might not understand what emotion they are feeling. Similarly, they may be able to recognize strong emotions in others, but may not know how to respond to these strong emotions appropriately.

However, not every child with autism has alexithymia, and alexithymia does not cause autism. Therefore, there must be other ASD-related symptoms that cause children to appear as though they lack empathy. Some of these symptoms may include poor eye contact, the inability to pick up on social cues, as well as the inability to read nonverbal cues like facial expressions.

The good news for parents is that empathy is a skill that can be taught and developed over time. In studies where autistic patients were presented with roleplaying situations that were meant to elicit empathetic responses, the patients learned how to demonstrate empathy using words and appropriate gestures (Poquérusse et al., 2018). Researchers have also experimented with various methods of teaching children with autism empathy, which include a combination of prompting, modeling, and rewarding children for focusing on others' feelings with appropriate phrases, facial expressions, and tone of voice. Empathy can also be developed through therapies like CBT or animal-assisted therapy.

Differences in Gender

Children with ASD are more likely to experience emotional and behavioral problems than neurotypical children Studies suggest that as much as 84 percent of children with autism also battle with anxiety, and 47 percent battle with depression (Schenkman, 2020). In most cases, these emotional and behavioral problems improve slightly from childhood to adulthood.

Adolescent psychiatrist Emily Simonoff led an investigation looking into the behavioral conditions experienced by children with autism. Her team found that 70 percent of children with autism were diagnosed with additional psychiatric and behavioral conditions. Moreover, these conditions did not improve substantially from adolescence into early adulthood. Commenting on the findings she said, "You could plot with really quite good confidence from age 12 what someone was going to look like at age 23" (Schenkman, 2020).

When it comes to emotional regulation, which refers to the ability to control one's emotions, autistic girls were found to have higher emotional reactivity than autistic boys. The cause of the gender disparity is still unclear, although one study found that on average, autistic girls are diagnosed later than autistic boys. The delayed access to behavioral therapies can explain why autistic girls struggle with emotional regulation more than boys. However, therapies to improve emotional control are just as effective for autistic girls as they are for autistic boys.

Helping Children With ASD Recognize Their Emotions

There are many ways parents can teach their kids to become emotionally responsive and recognize emotions in others. Exercises to label or recognize emotion should be carried out in a safe and comfortable environment where children won't feel overwhelmed. It is extremely important that children aren't stressed or pressured when engaging in these exercises, as this might negatively impact their learning and confidence to apply these skills in real-life situations.

One of the simplest methods for teaching children with autism to recognize emotion is by playing facial recognition games. For instance, you can show your child a photo of an angry person and ask them to name the emotion. After naming the emotion, you can have a discussion about the possible triggers for their anger, which can give your child an opportunity to cultivate empathy.

When playing facial recognition games with photos, use images that have a clean background and show the person's face. Ideally, you want your child's focus to be on the facial expression being shown, not the background detail. The more exaggerated the facial expression is, the easier it will be for your child to recognize basic emotions.

When your child has learned how to recognize basic emotions using photos of people's facial expressions, you can show them photos that offer more detail and tell a story, such as a photo of a mother and child hugging each other in front of a large Christmas tree with many presents around them. This kind of photo would help your child associate a certain type of emotion (in this case, happiness) with an occasion like Christmas.

Structured activities provide a useful way of teaching children to recognize emotions. When creating structured activities for your child with autism, you can follow these helpful tips:

1. Choose Age-Appropriate Activities

When teaching your child emotional recognition, choose activities that are appropriate for their developmental age. Pay attention to the type of activity, the level of complexity, and the vocabulary and communication method used. For example, if your child is having speech delays, choose an activity with a communication method that will match their strengths. Make sure the instructions are clear and simple to follow, and if your activity requires a response from your child, ensure the response required is short and direct. For example, from observing a photo, all you might require from them is to name the emotion in a single word.

2. Focus On One Emotion at a Time

Children with neurodevelopmental disorders take longer to learn emotional and behavioral skills than typical children. Therefore, slow down the pace and work through each emotion one at a time. Avoid overwhelming your child with information, as this won't help them learn and remember how to recognize various emotions. It is better to take baby steps and spend some time on one emotion, so your child knows how to identify it in several contexts. You can also start by teaching your child to recognize the six basic emotions, then gradually introduce them to secondary and more complex emotions.

3. Make Learning Emotions Fun and Interactive

Play-based learning is an effective method in teaching your child new skills in early childhood. Ensure your activities are fun and allow your child to be creative and engage their five senses. For example, when using visual cards, you can ask your child to name an emotion they see with their eyes, pick up a photo card or point to one with their fingers, or imitate one of the facial expressions using their own expressions and gestures. You can also add a creative element to your activities by asking your child to draw or paint pictures of certain emotions.

4. Take the Learning Outdoors

While showing your child photo cards can help them recognize emotions on paper, it doesn't guarantee that they will be able to recognize emotions in real-life situations. It is important to use everyday life experiences as teachable moments. For example, when driving past a billboard, you can ask your child what emotion the people on the billboard are expressing. At the park, you can point out specific children, and ask your child what they believe the children are feeling. Using everyday scenarios to reinforce what you have taught your child can help them realize that emotions are always present wherever they go, in different life circumstances.

Moving on to Emotional Regulation

It is expected for children under the age of five to have frequent meltdowns. During those early years, children are still learning to identify and respond appropriately to emotions they feel within themselves, as well as emotions they recognize in others. However, children with ASD can continue to struggle with emotional regulation past the age of five.

Emotional regulation is the ability to manage emotions in response to triggering situations. It involves being able to calm your mind and body when upset, adjust your behavior according to the demands of the situation, and handle fear or anger without having an emotional outburst.

Parents can teach their kids how to regulate emotions by helping them slow down and be more mindful of their emotional reactions, as opposed to reacting impulsively. Of course, teaching a child with autism this kind of skill takes a lot of practice, patience, and positive reinforcement, since they are often feeling an array of emotions at any given moment.

Parents should also avoid sheltering their kids from triggering situations, but instead, coach their kids on how to manage uncomfortable emotions and walk away from each situation feeling more confident in their ability to overcome challenges.

For example, if your child becomes upset when having to sit down and complete their homework, it is better to help your child recognize their frustration and find healthy ways to work through it, rather than doing their homework for them. You might teach your child how to work in time intervals, practice breathing techniques, or celebrate the small wins they make as they work through their homework. You can check in on them every once in a while to assess their progress and offer positive feedback.

It is common for parents to expect quick results when teaching their children how to manage their emotional reactions, however, the reality is that skill-building, especially with children with autism, takes time. You won't succeed on the first attempt, but that doesn't mean your training isn't effective. Simplify your activities and praise the small steps your child makes in becoming more aware of their emotional reactions. Avoid doing the work for your child, but instead, give them the time and space to make choices on their own.

Ideally, you want your child to decide on the most appropriate emotional response to a situation by themselves and offer non-judgmental and positive feedback each time you see them trying. For example, if you notice your child trying to calm themselves down but unfortunately went into a full-blown tantrum, you can calm them down and then explain what went wrong, why it went wrong, and how they can respond the next time it happens. The language and tone of voice you use should be non-threatening and encouraging so that your child isn't afraid of making mistakes as they learn to self-regulate.

Validating your child's emotions is another way of explaining to them how they are feeling, which makes it easier for them to recognize their emotions and respond in an appropriate way. At each stage of your child's development, you can use emotional validation to help your child recognize and regulate their emotions. Below is an age-by-age guide to assist you:

1. Infants

Get your infant to listen to recordings of play songs so you can help them maintain a relatively content or neutral state. A study has shown that multimodal singing is more effective in calming a highly aroused 10-month-old baby than a mother's speech (Trehub et al., 2015). It also suggested that playing songs like "The Wheels on the Bus" are better at soothing infants and reducing stress than lullabies.

2. Toddlers

By the time a child reaches the 12-month milestone, they begin to understand that certain emotions are more appropriate in certain situations. However, since a child with autism is easily triggered or overwhelmed by changes in the environment, they tend to switch between three emotions: happiness, fear, and anger. When helping your child deal with fear and anger, distraction and modeling are the best strategies to apply.

Distraction involves providing another source of stimulation for your child to focus on to help them calm down and return to a neutral state. As they grow, you can teach them how to handle challenging situations without needing a distraction. Modeling involves teaching your child how to respond to a situation based on your own reaction. For example, if your child is afraid of a new person who has entered their environment, you can show your child through your positive body language, tone of voice, and engagement with the person that they are not dangerous.

3. Childhood

During the childhood years, children start to experience secondary emotions. This can feel extremely overwhelming for a neurotypical child, but even more distressing for a child on the spectrum. Parents play a crucial role in how children with autism learn to recognize and accept their big emotions. By either validating or invalidating a child's feelings, parents can either make their children feel safe or uncomfortable expressing and processing their emotions.

Ideally, parents should create an environment at home where children feel safe to express a range of emotions without feeling judged or wrong for doing so. For instance, when a child feels supported and validated in their anger, just as much as they are supported and validated in their excitement, they learn that being angry is normal and manageable.

Watch Out for Parental Stress

Raising a child who is on the spectrum can be stressful. Since a child with autism doesn't reach developmental milestones like other neurotypical children, they might lag behind in many aspects, such as speaking later than other children or being socially inept. Parents might feel a sense of guilt for not being able to provide their children with the kind of upbringing they had imagined for them.

As important as it is for children with autism to learn how to regulate their emotions, it is just as important for parents to learn emotional regulation too. This is because parents' stress can affect their parenting behaviors and the overall well-being of the family unit.

For example, an emotionally dysregulated parent cannot model healthy coping strategies to deal with difficult situations. This affects what the child learns as 'acceptable' and 'unacceptable' behaviors. Having a highly stressed parent who yells whenever they are feeling overwhelmed might cause the child to believe that yelling is one of the ways of dealing with frustration. Therefore, a healthy and emotionally regulated parent can model healthy coping strategies and teach their child rules and acceptable behaviors for displaying emotions.

There are different kinds of stressors parents may succumb to on a daily basis. Some might include driving their child to appointments, the challenges of getting an accurate diagnosis, and finding the best ways to soothe their highly aroused child. Parents may also be faced with different types of stress, including:

- **Psychological stress:** Parenting a child with autism can cause psychological distress and increase the risk of depression, especially when the parent doesn't have appropriate coping strategies in place or a support system they can turn to for emotional support.

- **Physical stress:** For some parents, symptoms of stress can be physical and lead to poor heart health, a weakened immune system, and gut issues. A parent with little to no support in raising and caring for their child with autism may also experience burnout, lose or gain appetite, and struggle with sleep.

- **Social stress:** Since many people are still misinformed about ASD and children on the spectrum, parents may have to deal with criticism from others, especially those who misunderstand their children's behaviors. As a result, some parents isolate themselves from others to avoid the stigma associated with autism and the stress may also put a strain on a couple's relationships.

- **Financial stress:** The cost of seeking medical assistance, special child care, and attending therapy sessions can become exorbitantly high and place a burden on family finances. The financial stress can be mostly felt in single-income and single-parent households where the majority of the medical expenses rest on one employed individual.

The good news for parents is that there are effective strategies to reduce or manage stress so that parenting a child on the spectrum feels less stressful. Here are a few below:

- **Make simple lifestyle changes.** Assess how you are currently living and make small adjustments to your daily routine to ensure you get sufficient sleep, eat nutritious meals, and schedule time for your hobbies and interests.

- **Ask for help.** Think of some tasks that you can delegate to other people so you can reduce the load of responsibility on your shoulders. Can you find someone trained to care for special needs children to take care of your child during the day? Or perhaps find hired help that can complete household chores twice a week so you can focus on other priority tasks.

- **Focus on the present moment.** Thinking about what your child has missed out on or the challenges they might face in the future can make you feel overwhelmed. Instead, stay grounded in the present moment and focus on the current needs of your child. Ask yourself: *What is my responsibility to my child and to myself today?*

- **Find social interests to help you recharge.** Work isn't and shouldn't be the only place you can take a break from your parenting responsibilities. You can find health-related or creative pursuits to boost your mood, help you relax, and give you an opportunity to socialize with other adults. Schedule a few hours on some weekends where you prioritize recharging and practicing self-care through engaging in social interests of your choice.

- **Find a solid support system.** Research has found that parents who have a healthy and strong support system are less likely to experience stress than those who don't have people to turn to. Close friends and family can form part of your support system, although school teachers, therapists, advocates of children with autism, and other parents raising children on the spectrum can be a part of your support system too.

- **Seek medical advice.** If you are struggling to manage your stress levels or find parenting your child overwhelming, reach out to doctors who can assess your physical, mental, and emotional well-being, and provide you with psychological tools and techniques on how to become a healthier and happier parent.

Sometimes, the most effective way to manage stress is to check in with yourself and assess how you are currently managing your stress and look for healthier approaches. You might have to commit to consistently practicing these healthier approaches for a few months before they become new habits.

Exercise: Helping Your Child Improve Their Emotional Regulation Skills

Emotional regulation can help your child adapt their behavior to difficult situations that may trigger anxiety, stress, or frustration. For this exercise, ensure your child is in a good state of mind and doesn't have any distractions around them. To avoid distractions, you can choose a quiet room in the house with fewer objects or things to grab your child's attention. It is also important to carry out this exercise only after your child has gained a basic understanding of identifying and labeling different emotions.

To begin, create an emotional levels chart similar to the one below:

Emotional level	"I feel this way when..."
Feeling good	

Emotional level	"I feel this way when…"
[Draw a simple illustration]	
A little upset [Draw a simple illustration]	
Upset [Draw a simple illustration]	
Very upset [Draw a simple illustration]	

You can choose to draw an illustration for each emotion to provide your child with a visual aid to help recognize each emotion. The second column should be left empty so that your child can write down their responses to each emotion. There are different prompts you can give your child to elicit different answers from them. Here are a few ideas:

- Ask your child to write down situations that trigger the various emotional levels.

- Present your child with a scenario and ask them how they would feel in that moment, referring to the emotional levels.

- Once the second column has been filled in, you can look at each response and ask your child whether they have assigned the appropriate emotional level. For example, you can say "I can see that you put 'not playing outside' as something that makes you very upset. Should it stay in this position or move up to another level? Perhaps 'a little upset' or 'upset?'"

- Look at the second column responses and ask your child how they would cope in each situation. For example, if they were upset because they had to do their homework, what would be the healthiest next step to take? You can present many coping strategies to your child, such as taking deep breaths, asking for help, talking to a teacher or parent, or thinking of something that makes them feel happy.

Play the emotional levels chart activity on a regular basis and assess how well your child matches an emotion with the appropriate response. They might not get it right the first few times, but eventually, you will notice your child being aware of the severity of various situations and choosing the best coping strategies to deal with each one.

Key Takeaways

It is common for children with ASD to experience difficulty identifying and labeling their and other people's emotions. Research has found that in some cases this is caused by a condition known as alexithymia, which is the inability to describe feelings. However, it can also be due to ASD-related symptoms like having difficulty reading social cues and facial expressions and not being able to express how they are feeling. Fortunately, empathy and emotional regulation are skills that can be learned through fun and interactive activities your child will love. They can also be taught through behaviors and coping strategies you model in front of your child.

However, as a parent, you should be prepared for times when the emotions your child feels get too big to handle. These emotional meltdowns are inevitable but can be managed by taking the necessary course of action. The following chapter will teach you how to manage outbursts that might look like bad behavior but are actually massive cries for help.

Chapter 5:

When ASD Behavioral Issues

Become Too Much

In this chapter you will learn:

- What happens inside the body of a child with ASD when they have an emotional outburst.

- How to limit the duration and impact of your child's meltdowns.

The Vagus Nerve and ASD

The parasympathetic nervous system (PSNS) is responsible for some of the main bodily functions, such as heart rate, breathing, immune response, digestion, and moods. When the PSNS is activated, your heart rate slows down, blood pressure drops, and you enter a restful state. Therefore, the more frequently your PSNS is activated, the more relaxed and balanced you will feel.

The PSNS can also be naturally triggered after a stressful situation. To get you out of the fight, flight, or freeze stress response, your body will activate the PSNS, so you can return to a calm and balanced state of mind and body. Without the activation of the PSNS, your body is unable to "switch off" the stress response and reverse the symptoms of hyperarousal.

There are three primary nerves, known as cranial nerves, in the PSNS. These are the vagus nerves, oculomotor nerves, and glossopharyngeal nerves. It is estimated that about 75 percent of all nerves found in the PSNS are vagus nerves. Vagus nerves are incredibly important because they help to regulate some of the main bodily functions. They have branches that lead to many vital organs, such as the stomach, kidneys, bladder, and reproductive organs. Moreover, the brain-gut connection is established through vagus nerves, which send information about the state of internal organs to the brain, so an appropriate response can be triggered.

The function of the vagus nerve is impaired in children with autism. Scientists have found that this is due to the heart rate (that usually accompanies breathing) being slower to develop. This makes it harder for children with autism to regulate their breathing and puts them in a heightened state of arousal. When children are aroused, they tend to feel stressed, even when they are not presented with any potential danger. Since the vagus nerve is impaired, it can be more difficult for them to self-soothe once the stress response has been triggered.

Imagine being at work and feeling yourself getting increasingly anxious. You might investigate where your anxious feelings are coming from and then proceed to calm yourself down. The difference with children with autism is they are not always aware of what might have triggered their strong emotions, but even when they are, they can find it extremely difficult to calm their nervous system and turn off the stress response. This is often the reason children with autism can take hours to calm down after having an unexpected meltdown.

Sensory Integration Disorder in Children With ASD

An impaired parasympathetic nervous system isn't the only thing that might cause a child with ASD to have unexplained and extended meltdowns. Another possible cause could be having a dysfunctional sensory system, known as sensory integration disorder. Sensory integration disorder occurs when one or more senses are either under or overstimulated.

Sensory integration is a natural process that begins in the brain before birth. The process involves integrating and interpreting sensory stimulation from the environment and organizing it appropriately in the brain. Children with sensory integration disorder, which may include children with neurodevelopmental disorders, experience a situation where sensory information is not organized properly in the brain. This leads to a host of problems in processing and responding appropriately to sensory input.

There are three main sensory systems responsible for sensory integration, which include the tactile, vestibular, and proprioceptive systems. These three senses are interconnected and also communicate with other parts of the brain. Dysfunction in these three sensory systems can lead to behavioral symptoms that are common among children with neurodevelopmental disorders, such as ASD. Here is an explanation of each sensory system and some of the common signs that they are not functioning properly:

1. Tactile System

The tactile sensory system includes nerves that are responsible for your child's sense of touch. These nerves usually live under the skin's surface and send information about physical touch, temperature, pain, and pressure to the brain. When the tactile sensory system isn't working properly, your child may experience the following symptoms:

- Being uncomfortable with physical touch

- Refusing to eat foods with certain textures

- Refusing to wear clothes with certain textures

- Finding it frustrating to have their hair or face washed

- Avoiding getting their hands dirty with mud, glue, paint, or other materials

A dysfunctional tactile system can lead to hypersensitivity and may cause your child to have negative emotional responses, like frustration or irritability, when being touched.

2. Vestibular System

The vestibular sensory system is made up of canals within the ear that are able to detect movement and changes to the position of the head. When the vestibular system is not functioning properly, your child may experience the following symptoms:

- Fearful of activities involving movement, like riding on a swing or going down a slide

- Finding it difficult to climb or go down stairs

- Feeling uneasy going down a steep hill, uneven surface, or sharp incline

- May appear clumsy due to fear of space and movement

Some children may continuously seek to stimulate their vestibular sensory system. These children are known to have a hyporeactive vestibular system and may seek intense and exhilarating experiences like spinning, jumping, and whirling around.

3. Proprioceptive System

The proprioceptive system is made up of components of muscles, tendons, and joints that make an individual aware of their body position. For instance, the proprioceptive system is responsible for ensuring your child sits upright on a chair and climbs down stairs in an orderly manner. It also allows your child to control objects, such as holding and writing with a pencil or feeding themselves with a spoon. When the proprioceptive system is dysfunctional, your child may experience the following symptoms:

- Frequently falling

- Clumsiness

- Unusual body postures

- Reluctance to crawl when they are young

- Reluctance to practice new motor movement activities

Children with autism tend to have an impaired parasympathetic system, which makes it harder for them to self-soothe when they are feeling agitated. On top of this, they may have an under or overstimulated sensory system that makes even the slightest forms of touch, sound, or movements feel irritating, uncomfortable, or threatening. For example, some children can't stand the feeling of Scotch-Brite, and others can't tolerate the smell of fish because it makes their stomachs churn. But for a child with ASD, the same sensation is severely multiplied and some sensory overloads can cause physical pain or meltdowns.

What Are Autism Meltdowns?

Children with ASD are prone to meltdowns, which on the outside, may appear as tantrums. Meltdowns can be defined as intense reactions to sensory overload. When a child with autism is overwhelmed with sensory information, the only way they know to express the overwhelming experience is to have a meltdown. It can manifest as a loss of control, which can be expressed verbally through screaming or crying, or physically through biting, kicking, or throwing objects.

Autism-related meltdowns are not the same as temper tantrums. Temper tantrums often occur when a child seeks the attention of their caregiver and engages in inappropriate behaviors to get what they want. In most cases, the child is too young to communicate their needs and chooses to "act out" as a way of having their needs met. The child might calm down once their caregiver gives them the attention they desire, or when they realize they are not going to get their way.

A child who throws a tantrum is aware of their inappropriate behavior and can adjust the severity of their tantrum depending on the circumstances. For example, if they are being ignored, their behavior may become worse, in order to elicit a response from their caregiver. Meltdowns, on the other hand, are triggered by sensory overload, not unmet physical or emotional needs. They also have a number of defining characteristics, such as:

- Your child may show pre-meltdown signs by rumbling

- Rumbling may be followed by stimming, which refers to engaging in repetitive behaviors in an effort to self-soothe

- The meltdown can be triggered by overstimulation or sensory input, such as uncomfortable fabric

- The meltdown typically lasts longer than a temper tantrum

Sometimes temper tantrums and meltdowns can come with aggressive behavior, such as punching, biting, or other acts of self-harm. A child with autism may resort to aggression when a familiar object is taken away, or when they are coerced into doing something they are uncomfortable doing.

When handling aggressive behavior, ensure the safety of your child and those around them. You can also remove the cause of aggression or give your child calming and familiar objects to play with as a form of distraction. Lastly, take a look at your environment and think of ways of making it feel safer for your child. In many cases, this means reducing the amount of sensory stimuli around your child. For example, if there is music playing, switch it off or play it softly in the background, or if the lights are bright, you can dim or switch them off. Additionally, your child may feel safer when left alone with you, so go into a quiet room where there aren't any small kids or adults around.

How to Manage Autism Meltdowns

How you manage a temper tantrum will be different than how you manage an autism meltdown. Let's first discuss how you can manage your child's tantrums.

When your child throws a tantrum, they often want something from you. Typically, they are demanding something that you have already refused them. Your child may not be comfortable adhering to boundaries or hearing the word 'no,' nonetheless, that doesn't mean you should give in to their demands. Remind yourself of the reason for refusing your child and follow these simple steps:

- **Remain calm and rational.** It can be really easy to lose self-control when your child is noticeably upset and their behavior is becoming increasingly uncontrollable. However, as their parent, you are responsible for modeling healthy behaviors and attitudes like being composed. Your calm demeanor can help your child slowly return to a relaxed state.

- **Don't feel pressured to give in.** When your child throws a tantrum, it can be just as uncomfortable for you as it is for them, especially when you are in a public space. While giving your child what they want can be a short-term solution to calming them down, it can backfire in the long run. Your child will learn that in order to get what they want, all they need to do is to throw a tantrum.

- **Validate your child's emotions.** Tantrums can be stressful for your child, especially when they are still too young to express their needs. Instead of telling them to stop misbehaving, acknowledge their feelings, but continue to stand your ground. For example, you might say: *"I know you are upset that you can't play outside, but it is raining and we don't play in the rain."*

When it comes to managing autism meltdowns, there are many different strategies you will find on the internet. This is because there isn't a one-size-fits-all approach to handling meltdowns. Your child may have specific likes and dislikes, making some strategies less effective than others. However, there are some general guidelines you can follow and customize to suit your child's needs. These are as follows:

- **Anticipate a meltdown.** Your child may show signs of a meltdown before it actually happens. You might see them pacing around, asking repetitive questions for reassurance, or rocking their body to and fro. You might be able to prevent the meltdown from occurring at this stage by removing specific sensory inputs, distracting or diverting your child's attention, or remaining calm yourself.

- **Identify the trigger.** Meltdowns are a result of an overwhelming experience in your child's environment. By identifying the source of overwhelm, you can immediately act by removing it from your child's environment. If you are not sure what the trigger may be, document what happens before, during, and after a meltdown. You might find patterns emerging, such as the time of day the meltdowns occur, or the particular setting they tend to occur in.

- **Give your child space if needed.** Placing your child in a quiet and safe room, like their bedroom, can help them calm down during a meltdown. If you are in public, you can return to your car or enter a restroom. It is not recommended to leave your child alone because this can make them feel unsafe. Your presence in the room, even if there is no eye contact or physical touch, can be reassuring.

- **Limit changes in your routine.** Having unpredictable and unstructured routines can make your child feel anxious and trigger a meltdown. If there is no way to avoid a change in routine (eg. Your child has a doctor's appointment), explain the upcoming changes in advance and reassure your child that the rest of the routine will stay the same. Use drawings, timetables, calendars, or other illustrations to explain the change and make your child feel comfortable with it.

- **Put yourself in your child's shoes.** When your child is having a meltdown, they are feeling extremely emotional and aren't thinking rationally. Their behaviors aren't logical and may be considered inappropriate for their age. Avoid trying to reason with your child because this will not help them calm down. Instead, remain calm and validate your child's emotional experience.

If your child is prone to meltdowns, preparation can help you divert the situation. Having a meltdown kit can be a great way to deescalate a situation and provide positive distractions for your child. A meltdown kit consists of objects your child enjoys playing with that can help them relax. A few items you can include in your child's meltdown kit are:

- Slime

- Fidget toys

- Kinetic sand

- Stress ball

- Sunglasses

- Legos

- Small musical instruments

- Stuffed animals

- Bubbles

- Puzzles

- Playing cards

- Noise-canceling headphones

Note that a meltdown kit is effective in preventing a meltdown and may not be able to calm your child once a meltdown has started.

Self-Stimulatory Behavior

Self-stimulatory behavior, also known as stimming, is repetitive behavior commonly displayed by children with ASD. It can involve movements like hand-flapping, rocking, or spinning. Stimming isn't considered destructive behavior, as it can be your child's way of regulating their body to avoid meltdowns. However, when stimming starts to interfere with other daily tasks and activities, it can become potentially harmful.

There are many reasons for stimming besides emotional regulation. Your child can stim as a way to express excitement, boredom, or distract them from sensory overload. By recording your child's specific stimming behavior, you can notice which behaviors they turn to when they are feeling a certain way. Perhaps when your child is in distress, they might make a humming noise or scratch their skin repetitively. Picking up on this behavior early enough will allow you to intervene before they become too overwhelmed.

There are some stimming behaviors that can be harmful to your child. These may include head banging, picking at their skin until it bleeds, or punching themselves. It is estimated that about 30 percent of children with autism engage in self-harming stimming behavior. Researchers believe that it is triggered by an enhanced expression of pain, such as when your child experiences a headache or stomach discomfort.

It is believed that children with autism do not feel pain while engaging in self-harming stimming behavior. The release of endorphins while expressing their frustration may provide an anesthesia-like effect and make them feel calm afterward. Nevertheless, these behaviors are dangerous and it is important to help your child find other ways of expressing their emotions.

Since children with autism have an impaired parasympathetic nervous system, they find it harder to regulate their heart rate when exposed to overwhelming stimuli. As a response to feeling vulnerable, they engage in self-stimulatory behavior to zone out and reduce feelings of stress. Researchers have found that healthy foods and supplements can support vagal tone (strengthening the vagus nerve) and reduce your child's sensitivity to the environment. Consult a doctor to run a metabolic laboratory test, so you can identify the nutrients your child needs to regulate their stimming behavior. Here are some of the nutrients your doctor may recommend:

1. Thiamine (Vitamin B1)

The vagus nerve starts at the medulla, which is found in the brainstem and connects the brain with the rest of the body. This region of the brain is vulnerable to thiamine deficiency and this can lead to vagus nerve dysfunction and gastrointestinal conditions, like constipation and stomach pain. Thiamine can be found in different sources of food, such as beef, pork, milk, eggs, nuts, seeds, and breakfast cereals containing vitamin B1.

2. Acetylcholine

The parasympathetic nervous system relies on acetylcholine to assist in bodily functions like digestion, salivary flow, gut motility, healthy bladder function, and tear formation.

Acetylcholine is also important for good brain health and can assist in improving learning and memory. Some of the foods that contain acetylcholine are eggs, butter, liver, peanut butter, whole grains, and vegetables.

3. Probiotics

A healthy gut can improve brain health by improving the function of the vagus nerve. Lactobacillus Rhamnosus, a probiotic strain, has been shown to enhance GABA receptors in the brain, which leads to reduced stress and lessens the risks of anxiety and depression. Foods that contain this particular probiotic strain include kefir, yogurt, sourdough bread, and sauerkraut.

4. Sulforaphane

Sulforaphane is believed to improve gene activity that protects cells against oxidative stress and inflammation. A 2019 study found that sulforaphane had a positive effect on the nervous system and was useful in managing anxiety and depression. The types of foods containing sulforaphane are broccoli, Brussels sprouts, cabbage, and cauliflower.

5. Magnesium

Many children with autism tend to be deficient in magnesium. Magnesium comes with a host of health benefits, such as inducing sleep, relaxing muscles, and preventing constipation. You can give your child magnesium supplements, taken together with vitamin B6, to provide greater support to their central nervous system.

Vagus Nerve Stimulation

A new technique has emerged that can help your child with ASD manage stress, decrease feelings of pain, and regulate their nervous system. This technique is known as vagus nerve stimulation and serves to counterbalance the body's natural fight-flight-freeze response.

What's great about vagus nerve stimulation is that it can be done at home by practicing relaxation exercises with your child. For example, you can teach your child how to take deep breaths to calm their mind and body, and regulate their heart rate. This will help to relieve stress and distract them from the triggering stimuli.

Here are simple breathing exercises you can teach your child at home:

- Inhale through your nose and exhale out your mouth

- Inhale for five counts and exhale for five counts

- Put your hand on your abdomen and feel it expanding as you inhale, and collapsing inward as you exhale

- Exhale longer than you inhale (it is the exhale that provides a feeling of relaxation)

There are other fun exercises you can try with your child to stimulate their vagus nerve. These include:

- Pour water in your mouth and make a gurgling sound

- Sing along to your child's favorite songs out loud

- Give your child a gentle foot massage

- Play fun games that make your child laugh (laughter boosts your child's moods and immune system, as well as stimulates their vagus nerve)

Key Takeaways

The vagus nerve is part of the parasympathetic nervous system and connects the brain to many vital organs. It is responsible for some of the main bodily functions like regulating heart rate and breathing. This function is impaired in children with autism, which means they are more likely to be in a constant state of hyperarousal. Besides vagus nerve dysfunction, your child may be easily overwhelmed due to sensory integration disorder, where typical sensory input like touch or sounds can lead to sensory overload. The end result is often an autism meltdown that lasts several hours and causes an overwhelming amount of stress and anxiety. Fortunately, meltdowns can be prevented by identifying triggering stimuli in your child's environment, validating their emotions, and finding ways to stimulate their vagus nerve.

After looking at emotions and behavior, it's much easier to understand why children with autism have a hard time in social situations. The next chapter looks at the consequences of delayed social interactions and what can be done to help.

Chapter 6:

The Importance of Developing

Social Skills

In this chapter you will learn:

- The importance of learning social skills for children with ASD.

- What social skills and typical milestones are, and what can be done to help children who struggle with social interactions.

What Are Social Skills?

Imagine how different your relationships would be if you didn't have any social skills. How would you handle yourself in a job interview? Or order a meal at a restaurant? During the peak of Covid-19 pandemic, families from across the world had to spend more time isolated indoors and away from other people. In some countries, like Spain, children were confined for three months at a time. Now that lockdown rules have become more lenient, both adults and children must re-integrate into society. This process will be especially difficult for children with ASD.

Social skills are the tools humans use to interact and communicate with each other for the purpose of building strong and healthy relationships. These skills are normally used in conjunction with emotional skills, such as empathy, to understand other people's thoughts and emotions.

It takes a long time for a child to learn social and emotional skills. In most cases, the average child begins by learning how to identify, express, and regulate their emotions. This involves using language to verbalize what they are feeling. They might also use nonverbal cues like facial expressions or body gestures to signal what they are experiencing.

From then onward, developing social and emotional skills is about having an awareness and appreciation for other people's emotions, as well as being comfortable exploring and interacting with the environment. This may also include being adaptable to different social settings, such as your child's ability to be quiet when visiting a library.

Your child's ability to develop social skills is important because it can help them build and nurture meaningful relationships with friends and family. It also makes them feel more confident exploring new social situations and becoming more independent. It is generally understood that the earlier your child learns social skills, the more equipped they will be to handle stressful situations as a teen and adult.

While schools can teach your child social and emotional skills, the role a parent plays in nurturing their child's early development can assist with learning crucial skills like listening to others, maintaining eye contact, practicing good manners, following instructions, and displaying self-control.

Social Skills Building Blocks

During the early years, your child learns social skills through the various forms of communication and interaction they have with you. They will watch how you respond to their needs and emulate the same behavior to others. For children with ASD who might take a little longer to develop social skills, focus on introducing one skill at a time, starting with awareness. Below are three building blocks for teaching your child social skills:

1. Awareness

Children must have an awareness of how their tone of voice, body language, and actions impact others. They should also learn how to decipher between positive and negative feedback. For example, praising your child for good behavior teaches them how to react to positive feedback, and setting healthy boundaries can teach them what unacceptable behavior looks like.

2. Emotional Self-Control

It is important for your child to learn how to calm themselves down so they can think of appropriate ways to respond to social situations. This skill can take a while to learn, but you can begin teaching your child emotional self-control by strengthening their levels of concentration, so they can maintain focus until they have completed a task. Later on, you can teach them how to maintain an emotion while completing a task or when visiting a public place, like the local park or grocery store.

3. Receptive to Language

Once your child is aware of how their actions impact others, and how to maintain or switch between emotions, you can teach them verbal or nonverbal communication to help them communicate their needs, wants, and desires. If your child hasn't started speaking, you can teach them how to point at objects, hold your hand and lead you to a location, or imitate certain facial expressions. Role-playing and providing prompts are additional fun ways of getting your child comfortable using language.

One of the most effective methods of modeling social skills is through play. Playing with your child fosters cooperation, attention, patience, taking turns, appropriate body language, and conflict management. Here are a few fun games you can play with your child to teach them social skills:

- **Role-playing upcoming social situations:** To reduce stress and anxiety about upcoming social events, role-play various scenarios that could happen. Take turns switching roles, so your child can practice stepping into someone else's shoes.

- **Play board games:** When you play board games with your child, you are teaching them how to wait their turn and maintain focus on the game. This can also teach them how to maintain an emotion for an extended period of time, as well as how to cooperate with others and bounce back from failure.

- **Read and discuss stories:** Read a book and stop to discuss the various social skills the characters display. You can comment on how the characters speak to one another, how they respect each other, and the outcomes of their actions.

- **Encourage family conversations:** When you are sitting around the dinner table or driving as a family in the car, ask a general question that each family member should answer. For instance, you could ask, "What was the best moment of your day?" You can use a stick to help your child identify who the speaker is. Encourage everybody to keep quiet while the speaker is holding the stick. Validate each response before moving on to the next speaker.

If you notice your child having difficulty learning the social skills building blocks, you can seek the assistance of a therapist. A speech therapist can help your child develop social skills using age-appropriate interventions, but if there are multiple areas of concern, you can consult with an occupational therapist.

Stages of Social Development

As your child grows and begins interacting with other children, you might wonder what social development milestones they ought to be reaching. Remember, when it comes to any kind of milestone, children won't necessarily reach them at the same time. Your child may be advanced or delayed at developing certain social skills, and this is normal. The only time you should have concern is when your child isn't reaching any of the expected milestones at all. In this event, reach out to a specialized child therapist who can evaluate your child and begin the process of therapeutic intervention.

When your child is a toddler between the ages of one and three, they might still test your boundaries and throw temper tantrums to get your attention. These signs are both normal and natural, and it is how your child starts out learning how to manage their big emotions. Below are a few strategies that can teach your toddler how to develop social skills at their age:

- Look for genuine ways to acknowledge your child's good behaviors, like when they share toys with their siblings or remember their good manners.

- Use positive statements when speaking to your child, such as saying please and thank you, and being reassuring after setting boundaries. For example, you might say, "It is Mommy's turn to speak now, then you can tell me your story afterward, okay?"

- Validate your child's emotions without taking away the consequences of their actions. Let them know that you understand what they are going through, and they will feel better soon.

- Look for opportunities to surround your child with other toddlers. Perhaps you can stop by the local park during the day so your child can interact with other kids. You can also set up regular play dates so your child is comfortable playing with others.

Eventually, your child will reach preschool age and they will require more advanced social skills. They will quickly learn that in order to connect with other children, they need to put themselves out there. Here are a few strategies you can use to teach your child social skills at their preschool-age:

- You can express your affection through appropriate physical touch. For example, if your child has done well on a task, you can ask them to give you a high five.

- Offer your child plenty of opportunities to make choices. This will teach them to become more independent and have high self-esteem. For example, you can allow them to choose between two shirts, two cups, two books to read, and so on. Afterward, praise them for making a good choice.

- Use role-playing to reenact common social situations. Help your child find the appropriate phrases to say in response to certain experiences, like being greeted by a stranger. This kind of practice can make your child more confident socializing with others in a real-life setting.

Whether you are teaching your toddler or preschooler how to demonstrate social skills, having educational and open-ended toys around the house can help to spark your child's imagination and experience what social play feels like. Examples of toys to have at your disposal include:

- Wooden alphabet blocks

- Arts and crafts supplies

- Magnetic tiles

- Role-playing clothes and accessories

- Large building blocks

What's great about these toys is that they are usually found in a classroom setting too, so your child can learn how to play these games alongside others or together. If you are playing with your child, create opportunities to take turns and collaborate in building a structure together. You can also assign your child a specific role while you take on another role and later combine your creations.

Professionals Who Can Help With Social Skill Development

The earlier you start training your child's social skills, the more comfortable they will be around people in social settings. Shortly after getting your diagnosis, you can look for medical professionals who can teach your child social skills depending on their individual needs. Since there isn't a doctor that specializes in treating ASD, you will need to consult with therapists who have extensive knowledge and experience in working with children with autism. We have spoken very briefly about these types of therapists in previous chapters. Below is a detailed look at what each one of them specializes in and how they can help your child:

1. General Practitioners

Your family doctor, or general practitioner (GP), is usually the first person you will consult on your autism treatment journey. They are able to listen to your concerns and recommend different interventions for supporting your child's development. Your GP can refer you to specialists who can take a closer look at your child and offer more structured support and training.

2. Psychiatrists

Since ASD is a developmental disorder that affects part of the brain, you are likely to meet with a psychiatrist along your journey. Psychiatrists specialize in analyzing and evaluating human behavior, as well as recommending treatment for mental health conditions. They often work alongside other specialists, such as psychologists and speech therapists to offer a detailed ASD diagnosis and assessment.

3. Psychologists

While psychiatrists are medical doctors who focus mostly on assessing mental health conditions, psychologists study human behavior and consider a child's intelligence, emotions, and motivations. They may offer a service known as psychotherapy, or talk therapy, where they help you or your child find solutions to social, learning, or communication challenges.

4. Occupational Therapists

An occupational therapist (OT) focuses on your child's overall health and well-being. Their job is to teach children with disabilities how to become more independent and feel confident undertaking daily tasks and social situations. OTs work closely with school teachers and parents to provide and implement strategies that will help children learn developmental skills.

5. Speech Pathologists

It is common for children with ASD to experience language and communication challenges. A speech pathologist can assess, diagnose, and recommend interventions for communication disorders. These interventions can focus on various challenges, like stuttering, language comprehension, reading, writing, and social behaviors that require communication.

Exercise: Social Interaction Skills Checklist

As a parent, you may be curious whether your child is progressing accordingly. This is a great concern to have because it ensures you catch any developmental delays in time and contact your GP if you notice little to no developmental progress.

Below is a checklist that you can use, courtesy of Kid Sense Child Development (2011). It will help you assess whether your child is reaching their social development milestones within the expected timeframe. Simply tick yes or no in the appropriate block. If you tick two or more boxes with a 'no,' contact your doctor and set up an appointment for a comprehensive evaluation of your child.

Age	Skill	Yes	No
0—6 months	Establishes eye contact for a few seconds.		
	Smiling when socially approached.		
	Laughing in response to playful behavior.		
	Calms themselves down after crying.		
	Picking up and playing with different objects.		
6—12 months	Playing peek-a-boo.		
	Clapping hands when prompted.		
	Spontaneously lifting arms to parents.		
	Spontaneously offer toys to others.		

Age	Skill	Yes	No
	Reacts to facial expressions.		
	Imitates an adult's actions.		
1—2 years	Identifies self in the mirror.		
	Spontaneously looking for missing objects.		
	Role-playing actions they've previously seen.		
	Imitating play related to their body (ie. Eating, taking a bath, or sleeping).		
	Saying simple words, like 'Hello,' 'Bye,' and 'Thank you.'		
2—3 years	Expressing their desires with phrases like, "I want a drink."		
	Treating stuffed animals as though they were alive.		
	Playing alongside other children.		

Age	Skill	Yes	No
	Beginning to use objects in an imaginative way (i.e. Pretending a stick is a magical sword).		
	Engaging in play themes that reflect less frequent life experiences, like going on holiday.		
3—4 years	Playing with mechanical toys.		
	Taking turns with other children.		
	Playing with two or three children in a group setting.		
	Talking about their feelings.		
	Feeling shame when reprimanded for doing the wrong thing.		
4—5 years	Having shared aims when playing with other children.		
	Using their imagination during play.		
	Engaging in games with simple rules.		

Key Takeaways

Social skills are essential for children with autism because they tie in with a lot of other essential life skills, such as academics and making friends. There is a range of social skills your child can learn, depending on their developmental age. Social skills building blocks like awareness, emotional self-control, and language recognition, can help your child become more confident in relating to others in social situations. Children with ASD may take a longer time to learn valuable social skills, however, it is possible. Your child can learn social lessons by observing your behavior at home, engaging in meaningful play, or attending goal-oriented therapy sessions.

When your child displays behaviors that are troublesome, but not related to ASD, they may be living with an undiagnosed condition like ADHD or anxiety. The following chapter will teach you various coping strategies when your child has been diagnosed with ASD and ADHD or anxiety.

Chapter 7:

How to Support Children With

Multiple Diagnoses

In this chapter you will learn:

- How to support a child who may be living with ASD and other related conditions, like ADHD or an anxiety disorder.

- Medication options for children with ASD with ADHD or anxiety.

The Reality of Multiple Diagnoses

Think for a moment about this hypothetical situation: You are convinced your child has autism, yet your teacher reports they are disruptive in class and find it difficult to sit still or complete work on time. Now you are a bit confused—does your child have ASD or ADHD? A third element is brought into the loop when your child struggles to make friends. Now you are left asking yourself: Does my child have ASD, social anxiety, or both?

When Daniel McKnight was three years old, he would often experience sudden bouts of anger. Since his behavior started when the family relocated, his parents believed it was an act of defiance. Little did they know that it was actually the first sign that their son was suffering from ASD and ADHD.

Daniel's active and often untameable behavior continued even when he started school. At times, his fits of rage would start early in the morning while preparing for school and carry on throughout the day. Teachers commented that Daniel was an unhappy kid who found it challenging to play with others.

Following a teacher's recommendation, Daniel's parents went to visit a psychiatrist. After an evaluation, the psychiatrist diagnosed him with an unspecified mood disorder and prescribed him antipsychotic medication. His troublesome behavior continued, and nine months later he was diagnosed with ADHD. This diagnosis explained why Daniel found it difficult to pay attention in class, although it didn't explain his seemingly random meltdowns. Senior school officials were forced to intervene and suggested to his parents that their son could be autistic too.

This made a lot of sense to Daniel's parents. Reflecting back on the early signs of their son's troublesome behaviors, they could sympathize with how distressful relocating to another state must have felt for their ASD and ADHD child. Since both conditions can be managed with a lot of structure and routine, the unexplained relocation must have felt like Daniel's entire world collapsing. Having received the two diagnoses, Daniel's parents placed him on an appropriate treatment plan and noticed his behaviors improving within months.

It can be frustrating for parents to determine which medical conditions their children are suffering from. In Chapter 3, we spoke more in-depth about the ASD-related conditions that could manifest as your child grows. Most of these related conditions are unrecognized and can interfere with the process of getting proper treatment.

There are doctors who believe that conditions like ADHD and anxiety come part and parcel with autism. The common symptoms of ADHD and anxiety disorders are so similar to ASD symptoms that doctors treat them as being aspects of autism, rather than being separate conditions. However, according to the DSM-5, doctors are urged to diagnose ADHD and anxiety disorders as co-morbid conditions, so autistic individuals receive the necessary medication and treatment plan.

Since the symptoms of ASD, ADHD, and anxiety disorders tend to overlap, it is difficult to assess what condition your child is experiencing without receiving a proper diagnosis. Nevertheless, there are certain observations you can make to understand your child's behaviors better so you can offer them the support they need. Below are three useful observations:

1. Look for Behavioral Changes and Challenges

One of the best ways to identify conditions of autism, anxiety, or ADHD, is to look for sudden or gradual behavioral changes and challenges. Document these changes over time, so you can easily pick up patterns in behavior. For example, over time, you may be able to distinguish between a tantrum and an autism meltdown or whether your child is shy, or if they have social anxiety. It won't be possible for you to identify the real issue by looking at isolated incidents, hence the need to document behavioral changes and figure out which condition they most resemble.

2. Look for Social Changes and Challenges

When your child changes schools, starts a new curriculum, or gets to know new people, they can experience stress and anxiety. However, this type of stress and anxiety is normal, and not necessarily a sign of ASD or anxiety disorders. More consistent social challenges, like avoiding groups of children, misbehaving, or saying awkward things in class, may be a sign of behavioral or developmental conditions. Remember, the social signs of ASD include difficulty reading social cues or responding to others' thoughts and emotions. The social signs of ADHD, on the other hand, are difficulty cooperating with others or taking turns. And lastly, the social signs of anxiety disorders include fear of humiliation, fear of failure, and withdrawal from others.

3. Look for Learning Challenges

Children with behavioral or developmental disorders often interpret things as being black and white, or right and wrong. They are unable to see things from another perspective or recognize nuances. Different kinds of learning challenges might be signs of either ASD, ADHD, or anxiety disorders. For example, having trouble paying attention is a classic symptom of ADHD, whereas having a tendency to give up on a task is a classic sign of anxiety.

Remember to document your observations so you can recognize patterns of behavior. While documenting the changes, ask your child's teachers for any feedback regarding their behavior in class. If your child is old enough, you can also ask them to give their input on typical tasks or behaviors they find challenging.

How to Manage Anxiety in Children With ASD

It is common for children diagnosed with ASD to also be diagnosed with an anxiety disorder. This is because the nature of autism can induce anxiety. For example, everyday life situations like eating breakfast, going to school, or socializing with other children can be stressful for a child with ASD and trigger anxiety.

One of the greatest causes of anxiety for a growing child with ASD is the fear of what others might think of them. As soon as your child reaches the age where they are more aware of their behaviors and how these might impact social relationships, they could feel more self-conscious around others. For example, if your child might struggle to make eye contact with others or strike up a conversation. This could lead to them having fears of being criticized or labeled as being strange by others.

Besides the fear of others' perceptions, there are also specific autism-related anxieties your child might have, such as:

1. Phobias

It is common for a child with autism to have certain phobias, such as the fear of food textures or certain objects. For instance, if your child has a fear of the color red, they might avoid eating red food, wearing red clothes, or being near objects with the color red. Or if they are afraid of people, they might panic when encountering strangers in public. The phobias your child has can interfere with their daily routine and cause them to live a rigid and restricted lifestyle. Working with an occupational therapist can help to ease your child's phobias over time.

2. Obsessive Compulsive Disorder (OCD)

A classic symptom of ASD is performing repetitive behaviors. This symptom can in some cases lead to obsessive and compulsive behaviors. You can identify signs of OCD in your child's behavior by looking at how they react when they are not performing their repetitive behaviors. For example, if your child gets frustrated when they are prevented from repeating certain behaviors or get upset when their repetitive behaviors are interrupted, they are displaying signs of OCD. Once again, therapy can be a great way to address these symptoms before they take over your child's daily life.

3. Social Anxiety

Children with ASD can display symptoms of social anxiety too. Social anxiety can be defined as the fear of being humiliated or judged in social situations. Since ASD makes it harder for your child to blend into social settings and confidently manage social interactions, they can become reluctant to be around other children.

The good news is you can help your child manage anxiety without taking any anxiety medication. Some of the practical interventions you can implement include:

- **Identify your child's anxiety triggers.** Knowing what exactly makes your child feel anxious is a great place to start. It can help you teach your child certain coping strategies to practice when they are feeling anxious. This also provides you with information that you can share with your child's teachers and therapists so they understand how to support them.

- **Introduce visual schedules and discuss upcoming transitions.** You can reduce your child's anxiety by offering them plenty of information about their daily schedule and what to anticipate. Think of different ways of presenting the information to your child, such as writing it down, adding photos, and even offering video tutorials. The more prepared your child feels about their daily activities, the more calm and confident they will be.

- **Create safe spaces around your home.** It is important for your home to feel like a sanctuary for your child. When they are not in the mood for being around family members or guests, ensure there is a room or area they can retreat. At school, your child's safe space could be the reading corner or another calming area. Note that a safe space isn't supposed to prevent your child from interacting with others, but instead to become a place they can temporarily go to when feeling overwhelmed.

- **Teach your child relaxation techniques.** When you are not around, your child will need to know how to self-soothe. Teaching them relaxation techniques, like breathing exercises or mindfulness, can help them reduce their stress levels. Find age-appropriate relaxation techniques online that are simple enough for your child to practice in your absence.

- **Create different social narratives.** Social narratives are a great way of preparing your child for what is going to happen through storytelling. While the story should be engaging, it must include factual information to help your child anticipate what a certain place or event will feel like. Repeat the story as often as you can, and provide visual cards (if necessary) so your child can follow by looking at the images.

How to Manage ADHD in Children With ASD

ADHD can cause daily challenges that affect your child's ability to learn, complete tasks, and control impulsive behaviors. It is important to begin addressing signs of ADHD while you wait to receive a diagnosis. The earlier you can start teaching your child effective coping strategies, the less disruptive their daily routine will be.

Before we discuss coping strategies, it's worth reiterating what ADHD actually looks like. In general, ADHD causes deficits in executive functions, such as thinking, decision-making, organization, or planning ahead (time-keeping). This means that your child may find it difficult to make choices on their own, complete chores or school tasks, or follow instructions. As a parent, you may find yourself having to guide your child, even to the point of micro-managing them, despite them being at the age to make decisions for themselves.

It is also important to be aware of behaviors that are typically seen as rude that are associated with ADHD. For example, your child might be watching TV and not hear you when you are calling their name. You may feel hurt because they are ignoring you, but it may be due to their inability to pay attention. Another example is telling your child to tidy their room, but when you enter their room it looks like they haven't made any improvements. Since children with ADHD can become distracted easily, they may have forgotten to clean their room once they got inside and found a really cool toy to play with instead.

Living with ADHD is just as stressful for your child as it may be for you and your family. By working together, you can make your household a safe and supportive environment for your child, and enforce norms and boundaries around your home that bring a sense of peace and stability to the whole family.

Parenting a child with signs of ADHD requires you to display both compassion and consistency. Below are a few ways you can do just that:

1. Maintain a Positive Attitude

Your child relies on you to model acceptable behaviors. When you take the time to work on your own moods, you can positively influence the moods of everyone around you. Since your child may feel anxious easily, they depend on you to be calm, so you can help them regulate their emotions. Remember to keep things in perspective and understand the realities of ADHD and how it might affect your child's behaviors.

2. Make Time for Self-Care

The best way to maintain a positive attitude is to make time for yourself. This can be as simple as dedicating 30 minutes to reading, enjoying a hot bubble bath, or going out for a quick coffee with a friend. Staying active through playing sports or physical exercise can also help you reduce stress and uplift your mood. If you don't already have a support system, it may be a good idea to start thinking about the people you can contact for medical and emotional support.

3. Create Structure and Hold Yourself Accountable

Your entire family can benefit from living in a structured and predictable home environment. Your child with ADHD will also appreciate having a predictable routine to follow. When creating structure for your family, think about the daily tasks that involve everybody, such as eating meals together, driving to school, doing homework, and so on. Ensure that these tasks occur at the same time each day so your family can get used to following a rhythm.

For your child, create a routine that is manageable to follow. Avoid including too many activities because these may cause distractions. You might also find that after certain times of the day, your child is less willing to focus. Therefore, organize their daily tasks, placing high priority tasks (or tasks requiring a great deal of focus) at the start of the day—or when your child is most alert.

4. Encourage Your Child to Stay Active

If your child has been diagnosed with ADHD, they are most likely hyperactive. This isn't necessarily a bad thing, as long as their energy is utilized properly. For example, giving your child plenty of time for outdoor or indoor movement activities can ensure they burn a lot of energy. This can make it easier for them to sit down for meal times or follow a sleeping schedule.

5. Create a Relaxing Bedtime Routine

Your child needs sufficient quality sleep to maintain concentration throughout the day. Without proper sleep, they are more likely to be irritable, restless, and find it difficult to focus on tasks. A bedtime routine can slowly prepare your child's mind and body for sleep. A typical bedtime routine consists of relaxing activities you can practice with your child before bed. These activities may include coloring a picture, listening to an audiobook, enjoying a warm bubble bath with toys, or playing quietly. You can also prepare the home for bedtime by dimming the lights, playing calming music in the background, switching off the TV and other electronic devices, and encouraging your family to speak quietly.

Medication for Anxiety and ADHD

Children with ASD can take a variety of medications to treat symptoms of anxiety and ADHD. However, the challenge that many parents face is receiving the right medication for the right symptoms. For example, a child who struggles to concentrate due to their anxiety might be given ADHD medication, rather than anxiety medication.

The cost of misdiagnosing a child's symptoms can cause harmful side effects and delay your child getting the proper treatment they deserve. For example, prescribing an anxious child a stimulant, which is typically ADHD medication, can cause digestive problems, make it harder for them to sleep at night, and in some cases, worsen their feelings of anxiety. Therefore, it is extremely important to understand the type of medication doctors prescribe to your child and whether they are targeting the correct symptoms.

If your child is struggling with anxiety, there are different types of medication that can help them manage their symptoms. The first are selective serotonin reuptake inhibitors (SSRIs), or antidepressants, which increase the levels of serotonin (the feel-good chemical) produced in the brain and are non-addictive. Antidepressants generally have few side effects, but a child may experience drowsiness, weight loss, and headaches. Another type of medication doctors may prescribe are benzodiazepines, which are used less frequently than antidepressants, but can treat acute anxiety. Children can build a tolerance to these kinds of medications and heavier doses are required for long-term treatment.

When it comes to treating symptoms of ADHD, doctors often prescribe stimulant medication, like methylphenidate or amphetamine. These two stimulants are considered among the safest psychiatric medications and come with very few side effects. However, some of the common side effects children may experience include weight loss, headaches, and difficulty falling asleep.

When deciding the correct dosage of stimulants, doctors will determine how well your child's body metabolizes the medication. In general, all doctors will start with a low dosage and then increase it every few weeks, until the optimal dosage is reached. Some doctors may even alternate between different stimulants to assess which one works the best. Stimulants like Adderall X, Evekeo, or Vyvanse can cause a negative reaction when combined with other medications. Therefore, be sure to let your doctor know which other medication your child may be taking.

As effective as a stimulant medication is, it is not guaranteed to work on every child. Some children may not respond to the medication, or the side effects may be too uncomfortable to manage. Furthermore, stimulant medication may not be appropriate for children who take inhaled steroids for asthma, suffer from borderline personality disorder (BPD), have a history of seizures or any heart conditions, or have an eye condition.

If you are hesitant about giving your child medication for anxiety or ADHD, you can consider alternative therapies, such as cognitive behavioral therapy (CBT). This evidence-based treatment has been found to be an effective psychological intervention that can improve your child's problem behaviors and teach healthy coping skills.

Exercise: Mindfulness Activities to Manage Stress and Anxiety

Whether your child is living with ASD, ADHD, or an anxiety disorder, a common challenge they will have is managing stress and anxiety. Teaching your child mindfulness can help them work through uncomfortable thoughts and feelings, so they can improve their level of focus and feel more confident carrying out tasks.

Mindfulness is a mind-body technique that teaches individuals how to become more present and pay attention to the experiences unfolding in each moment. Doing this can reduce stress and anxiety because it encourages your child to focus on real life events, rather than entering spirals of negative thought or being distracted.

The following activities offer a great way to bond with your child while teaching them how to become more mindful and reduce feelings of stress and anxiety:

1. Describing Sensations

Hand your child a few interesting objects, each having a different texture. Include rough objects like stones and smooth objects like a round ball. Ask your child to spend a few minutes holding the object in their hands and thinking about what it feels like. Thereafter, ask them to tell you what each object feels like.

2. What Do You See?

Sit down with your child and ask them to look around the room at all the wonderful items on display. Tell them to look for new objects they have never paid attention to before. Encourage them to look carefully and consider the finer details in furniture pieces, artwork, or accessories.

3. Focusing on Breathing

Ask your child to sit down in front of you or lie down on the floor. Tell them to close their eyes and breathe in through their nose and out their mouth. You can tell them to imagine they are in a park or forest, and the slow and gentle breathing is like the sound of wind blowing.

Key Takeaways

It is common for a child with ASD to be diagnosed with another condition, such as ADHD or an anxiety disorder. The symptoms of these three conditions can be similar, which makes diagnosing them a lot harder. However, there are behaviors you can observe from your child that are indicators of either ASD, ADHD, or anxiety. You can also address the symptoms of each condition separately, as part of an all-encompassing treatment plan.

Is there a treatment for ASD? Even though there isn't a known cure, there are different strategies and therapies that can help children with autism develop the necessary skills. There are also some crucial coping methods that will help all carers involved—all of which we will look at in the next chapter.

Chapter 8:

ASD Treatment Options

In this chapter you will learn:

- The different therapies for ASD so that you can discuss the possibilities and different options with your specialists.

Behavioral Therapies

ASD is a condition that affects a child's social behavior and early skills development. One of the most popular interventions for improving symptoms of ASD is behavioral therapy. It can help with learning social skills, attention-oriented play, and managing anxiety, with a focus on parent interaction (parents are taught strategies to use at home). There are four types of behavioral therapies, each presenting unique techniques that you can explore with your child.

Applied Behavior Analysis

Applied Behavior Analysis (ABA) is a behavioral therapy based on the science of behavior and learning. It can help parents understand how their child with ASD's behavior works, how learning takes place, as well as how their behavior and learning are affected by the environment. ABA therapy also has a practical component. It teaches language, communication, and concentration skills, and works on correcting challenging behaviors.

ABA therapy involves different kinds of techniques for understanding and modifying your child's behavior. Your therapist can adjust each technique to suit your child's needs, and skills can be taught in a group setting or on a one-on-one basis. Two common techniques used in ABA therapy are positive reinforcement and another known as "Antecedent, Behavior, Consequence (ABC)."

Positive reinforcement entails rewarding good behavior as a way to encourage the child to repeat the behavior again in the future. ABA therapists believe that when good behavior is incentivized, it is more effective in bringing about positive change. Positive reinforcement begins by identifying a goal. Each time the child reaches the goal by displaying certain behaviors, they are rewarded. The reward always carries some significance to the child, so that it becomes memorable. Over time, the child learns to demonstrate the desired behavior without requiring consistent rewards.

ABC is a technique that teaches parents why their child performs certain behaviors. It looks at what occurs before the behavior takes place (the antecedents), the actual behavior, and the consequences that follow. Learning this technique can teach parents how to prevent certain behaviors, like meltdowns, from taking place or, alternatively, they can help parents teach their children more appropriate behaviors.

For example, here is how the ABC technique can help you understand how a meltdown started:

Antecedent: You walked to the park with your child. There were a lot of children playing in the jungle gym, screaming and cheering.

Behavior: Your child started to make a humming noise, which was followed by restless behavior.

Consequence: They entered a meltdown and you decided to go home.

Here is another example of how the same technique can help you teach your child more appropriate behavior:

Antecedent: You walked to the park with your child. There were a lot of children playing in the jungle gym, screaming and cheering.

Behavior: You pulled out your meltdown kit and sat a distance away from the other children while your child self-regulated.

Consequence: Your child was able to play with their favorite toys while enjoying the energy and activity of the other kids at the park.

A board-certified behavior analyst (BCBA) is responsible for designing your child's unique ABA program. Some of the factors they might consider when designing the program include your child's needs, skills, preferences, interests, as well as your family situation. All of the information they collect from you will help them create treatment goals. Examples of possible treatment goals include:

- Social skills

- Motor skills

- Hygiene and self-care

- Play and leisure

- Language and communication

- Academic and learning skills

Your child's ABA program will also come with a clear instruction plan that breaks down each skill and the steps you can take to practice them at a comfortable pace. After each therapy session, the BCBA will evaluate your child's progress toward their treatment goals.

Relationship Development Intervention

One of the newest approaches to treating symptoms of autism is the Relationship Development Intervention (RDI). It focuses primarily on training parents and other caregivers on ways to support children with autism in their social and communication development.

Unlike ABA therapy, there are a few medical studies that back up the effectiveness of this approach. However, since RDI is very similar to ABA in that it also offers parents a custom treatment plan with specific social and behavioral goals, the results of the intervention can be measured over time. The only difference between RDI and ABA is the individual who leads the intervention. As discussed before, a trained ABA therapist leads the ABA therapy. They must have completed specific educational requirements and received certification through the Behavior Analyst Certification Board (BACB).

In contrast, parents and caregivers are empowered and trained by RDI consultants to lead the intervention. RDI providers might also offer books, seminars, and training classes that parents can attend. RDI techniques are designed to be used at home by the people most trusted by the child. Teachers and other educational administrators can also benefit from learning the RDI approach, so they can understand how this intervention can improve their relationships with autistic learners in the classroom.

The founder of the RDI, Dr. Steven Gutstein, discovered that exercising the child's dynamic intelligence can increase social awareness through natural interactions between close relatives. Strengthening the child's dynamic intelligence involved three components:

- Understanding other people's perspectives or acknowledging different opinions.

- The ability to cope with change, whether it is small or large changes.

- The ability to integrate information from different sources or multiple senses, like appreciating the smell and flavor of food.

The aim of RDI is to adjust inflexible thinking over time and encourage sharing of experiences. To achieve these aims, RDI focuses on six principles, which are:

- **Emotional referencing:** Learning from the subjective experiences of others.

- **Social coordination:** Knowing how to control and adjust behavior to improve social interactions.

- **Declarative language:** Making use of verbal and nonverbal communication to strike conversations, express empathy, and talk about subjective experiences.

- **Flexible thinking:** The ability to adapt to changing circumstances smoothly.

- **Relational information processing:** Sorting information into a workable context to solve problems creatively (without black or white thinking).

- **Foresight and hindsight:** Knowing how to extract lessons from past experiences, and use these lessons to make wise decisions about the future.

At the beginning of the intervention, parents will spend time building a trainer-trainee relationship with their children. Once this relationship has been established, they will move on to the treatment plan where they will put the six principles into practice.

To find an RDI consult, visit the RDI Connect website and make your selection from one of the many RDI certified program consultants. You can also visit the Autism Speaks website and look for an RDI consultant under the directory for autism services.

Sensory Integration Therapy

A 2013 study found that sensory integration therapy can improve the daily function of children living with autism (Schaaf et al., 2013). It has been proven to change how sensations are processed in the child's brain, and as a result, manage symptoms like sensitivity to sounds, lights, smells, textures, and flavors.

A typical scenario of how sensory integration works goes as follows: A parent and child will visit an occupational therapist (OT) who is qualified in administering the therapy. Some of the challenges the child may be facing include difficulty bathing or dressing, having rigid eating habits, or getting frustrated when their hands become dirty. In most cases, these challenges cause so much stress and anxiety for the child that they begin to interfere with daily functioning.

The OT will listen to the parent's concerns and evaluate the child's sensory system. They might even ask the parent to fill out a questionnaire to figure out which sensory systems are dysfunctional. Through fun and interactive games and exercises, the OT will attempt to change how the child's brain responds to touch, sounds, lights, and movement.

OTs have the knowledge and experience to design custom exercises to stimulate your child's senses. Every session will look different, depending on your child's needs and the kinds of activities the OT chooses to play. For example, in some sessions, the OT may start off by guiding your child through an obstacle course to strengthen joints and muscles and reduce any tension in the body. This activity may be followed by playing inside a ball pit to activate the tactile system, or picking up toys from a bucket of water to get your child used to feeling different textures.

There are many therapists who claim to offer activities related to sensory integration but are not trained as occupational therapists. To perform sensory integration therapy, a medical professional must undergo the proper training to become an occupational therapist. When setting up your appointment, ask your therapist whether they have completed the relevant OT training and courses. You can also read documents published by the American Occupational Therapy Association to familiarize yourself with this particular form of therapy and how it is supposed to be administered.

Communication Interventions

Communication can be defined as the exchange of verbal or nonverbal information to convey specific ideas, thoughts, and feelings. Communication can also be expressed in written form through reading books or writing ideas down.

Children with autism have varied experiences with communication, although many children with autism experience difficulty communicating in social settings. For some, speech and language skills may be delayed, and for others, these skills may be underdeveloped or don't develop at all.

Some children with autism who have the ability to speak may find it difficult to hold a conversation, understand social cues, or read other people's facial expressions. When engaging in conversation, they might also take things literally and struggle to understand sarcasm or figurative language. Children who are confident in speaking may have preferences for certain topics, particularly those they are obsessed with, and share a lot of detail–too much information for neurotypical people to grasp at one time.

Research suggests that early communication interventions can help in building communication and social interaction skills. A speech therapist can assist your child in developing these skills. They can also provide you with strategies that you can practice at home to support your child's speech and language development, such as recommending visual supports.

Visual supports are tools that help your child develop language skills. They can include any type of visual representation, such as photos, symbols, written words, or objects to help your child learn how to process information and understand language. You can ask your child to point to an image when they want to convey a message about it. For example, if they are hungry, you can teach them to point at the refrigerator. As your child discovers more words and phrases, you can teach them how to convey a simple message while pointing at an object.

When practicing communication exercises at home, remember the following tips:

- Be mindful of your own communication style, language, and tone of voice you use. Practice speaking more clearly, slower, and using the kind of language you desire your child to also learn.

- Avoid using nonliteral language, such as idioms, metaphors, or humor, which might have multiple meanings and isn't easy to interpret.

- Ask your child specific questions to elicit straightforward and simple answers. If you have misunderstood your child's message, ask more questions to get a simple 'yes' or 'no' answer.

- When giving your child instructions, break down the information into chunks. You can list each step in chronological order so the information is easier to process. Feel free to provide your child with visual support in the form of diagrams or written lists, so they can remind themselves of the instructions given.

Education and Learning Programs

Education and learning programs for children with autism often occur within schools and take on a "whole life" approach to learning and reasoning skills. Programs can include visual tools in the classroom or applied behavior analysis. Below are two effective programs that can address your child's learning needs.

TEACCH

TEACCH, which stands for the Treatment and Education of Autistic and related Communications Handicapped Children, is a program that seeks to strengthen the skills and strengths your child already has and support their development. While TEACCH is suitable for autistic individuals of all ages, how it is used depends on the child's specific age. For example, it can be used to assist in your toddler's early development but may improve your teen's interpersonal skills.

The TEACCH program was developed in the mid-1960s in the United States by an autism researcher named Eric Schopler. The program seeks to enhance existing strengths and provide training for areas of difficulty. Before the program begins, your child will be evaluated to determine their developmental level. Thereafter, they will receive a program that is customized to their needs.

Unlike other therapies that can be administered at home, TEACCH is administered at an early intervention center, using a structured teaching approach in a group setting. During each class, your child will complete various activities consisting of a mixture of individual learning, group activities, skill-building, and playtime. Each child's schedule will look different depending on their needs; however, as children gain more skills, their environment will become less structured.

Educators who desire to use the TEACCH method must receive training and certification from the TEACCH organization. Parents are advised to play an active role in supporting their children's learning and become 'co-therapists.' Nevertheless, the core teaching will be guided by a qualified instructor. There are five components or principles of TEACCH that educators will focus on during classes:

1. Physical Structure

Educators pay attention to your child's environment and
enforce clear boundaries to make the learning process feel
more comfortable for your child. For example, they will follow
a structured schedule throughout the day and divide the
classroom into different functional spaces, such as having an
area to play and another area to learn. Having physical structure
can help your child with autism become more organized and
make the environment feel more predictable.

2. Consistent Schedules

Consistency is key when teaching ASD learners. Not only can it
help them learn how to manage their time, but it can also make
them feel relaxed in the classroom. To reduce stress and
anxiety, it is important for an ASD learner to know what is
coming next and for the teacher to limit as many changes to the
routine as possible. One of the ways teachers can maintain
consistency is to follow a schedule and provide written and
verbal communication to explain the daily routine.

3. Establishing Expectations

The third principle of TEACCH is to establish expectations
with learners. Having clear expectations makes it easier for
teachers, parents, and other caregivers to create boundaries,
enforce consequences, and plan for interventions when
expectations are not met. Expectations also help to measure
each child's progress and encourage independent work. Before
activities, expectations are reviewed to help learners follow
instructions and feel confident completing each activity.

4. Maintaining Routines

Routines are what help the classroom environment feel safe and predictable for the ASD learner. When a child with autism is given a task or expected to do something outside of their routine, they can feel ambushed and distressed. This could make them withdraw or become uncooperative in completing the task, and in extreme cases, can lead to meltdowns.

5. Implementing Visual-Based Cues

Visual-based cues are created to be used in conjunction with verbal communication given by the educator. The visual cues could be written on a piece of paper, on a computer, or presented as illustrations. These visual cues are great to use with children with autism, especially those who are still improving their speech and language skills. They can also serve as reminders about classroom expectations and daily schedules, or to help children express their feelings.

Profectum Developmental, Individual Difference, Relationship-based Model

The Profectum Developmental, Individual Difference, Relationship-based Model (DIR) was developed by Dr. Stanley Greenspan and Dr. Serena Wieder. It places relationships at the forefront of emotional and cognitive development for children with autism. In particular, this model emphasizes the importance of the parent-child relationship to set the tone and create the foundation for the child's development.

Another name for DIR is floortime relationship-based therapy. This is because throughout the intervention, the parent is usually interacting with their child on the floor. During floor time, the goal is for the parent to support their child's development in many areas, such as emotional regulation, communication and language skills, cognition, motor skills, and social problem-solving. A parent is encouraged to not only get on their child's level physically but to also understand their child's developmental age and work on building their strengths.

The child gets to decide which games to play and their parents follow. However, every now and again, the parent will guide their child into more complex games or interactions, to expose them to new experiences. Each session on the floor should consist of back-and-forth play, so the child can learn how to focus on another person's experience, engage in problem-solving, and maintain focus throughout the interaction.

For example, if a child decides to play with a stuffed animal, the parent can pick up another stuffed animal and perhaps speak to it. This would be done to encourage the child to imitate the parent's behavior and speak to their stuffed animal too. Or alternatively, the child may be playing with a toy car and the parent might pick up another toy car and zoom past in front of the child's car, ultimately blocking their path. This would encourage the child to think of a response to either challenge the parent or find another creative way of getting ahead.

DIR programs will often have specific goals designed to achieve each DIR developmental level. The sessions are monitored and goals are adjusted when the child shows developmental progress. There are nine functional developmental levels that your child will be assessed on:

1. **Shared attention/Showing interest in the world:** Your child's ability to regulate their attention and show interest in a wide range of stimuli in their environment.

2. **Engagement/Forming relationships:** The depth and range of your child's interest and pleasure in interacting with others.

3. **Purposeful, two-way interactions, with gestures:** Your child's ability to communicate simple messages and maintain focus and interest when engaged in an activity.

4. **Purposeful, two-way, problem-solving interactions:** Being able to communicate patterns of thinking, negotiating, and developing their sense of self or independence.

5. **Elaborating ideas:** Assessing your child's ability to create mental representations, and exercise their imagination or use pretend play to share their own ideas with others.

6. **Building bridges between ideas:** Making connections between different emotional ideas, such as having the ability to say, "I am angry because you were mean to me." This sort of higher-level thinking helps your child separate fantasy from reality and learn to deal with challenges in more practical ways.

7. **Multi-cause, comparative, and triangular thinking:** Your child's ability to explore multiple perspectives or reasons for feeling a certain way and recognize the complexity of their feelings.

8. **Emotionally differentiated thinking:** Your child's understanding of shades of gray among emotional

states and that sometimes they might experience conflicting emotions, like being sad yet relieved that something happened. Your child may also start learning the consequences of their social behaviors and begin to define themselves by how well they are received by others.

9. **Intermittent reflective thinking:** Your child's ability to reflect on their feelings about relationships with friends and family. They may start to internalize certain values and strengthen their sense of self (which can be threatened by rejection from their peer group).

Medication

As mentioned at the beginning of the book, there are no known cures for ASD. However, some parents may seek medication to treat symptoms of ASD. These kinds of medications often treat three main autism symptoms: communication challenges, difficulty with social interactions, and repetitive behaviors. Parents should note that there are very few FDA-approved medications available on the market and not all of these medications will work on every child with ASD.

The two FDA-approved medications are risperidone and aripiprazole. They mainly treat symptoms related to irritability, but they can ease the other three main symptoms of autism (reducing irritability can make your child more sociable, etc.) The majority of the medications prescribed to children with ASD are marked as "off label," which means they are FDA-approved, however, are mostly prescribed for other ASD-related conditions like sleep disturbance and ADHD.

An example of this would be selective serotonin reuptake inhibitors (SSRIs), a class of medication that has been FDA-approved to treat anxiety disorders and depression. Clinicians have found that SSRIs can ease anxiety in children with ASD and make it easier for them to engage with others in a social context. Another example is naltrexone, which has been FDA-approved to treat alcohol and opioid addiction but can ease repetitive and self-harming behaviors in some adults and children with ASD.

It is important to note that these medicines won't necessarily work on every child with ASD and that all medicines come with side effects. Over time, your child may also build a tolerance for certain medications that will impact the medicine's effectiveness. It is important to consult with a doctor before putting your child on any medication and ask about the possible side effects.

Speech Therapy

Nearly every child diagnosed with autism will be referred to a speech therapist. This is because many children on the spectrum have delayed, limited, or no speech at all. Speech therapy helps children with autism learn how to use words to string sentences, but even more than that, it can teach them how to understand everyday language and use it appropriately.

Speech therapy is administered by a certified speech-language pathologist who holds a master's degree. They may run a private practice or operate from a local clinic or school. These therapists are trained to use specific tools, like toys or tests, and speech curricula to teach children how to communicate.

Depending on your child's communication needs, a speech therapist may focus on improving the following skills:

- **Nonverbal communication skills:** Teaching nonverbal gestures, using visual representations, and other nonverbal communication tools like electronic talking devices.

- **Observing body language:** Teaching different bodily cues and movements that indicate how the other person is feeling, whether they are open or closed off to conversation, and when it is safe or unsafe to engage with others.

- **Asking and answering questions:** Learning how to decipher between a question and a statement, and how to formulate responses to questions or create unique questions.

- **Prosody:** Learning how to create melody when speaking and changing tone of voice to avoid sounding flat or monotonous.

- **Social skills:** Teaching social communication skills, such as maintaining a back-and-forth conversation, expressing abstract ideas and concepts, and assessing the mood of the room or person being spoken to.

While you wait to find the right speech therapist for your child, there are a few techniques you can practice at home that are based on three principles of speech therapy, which are as follows:

1. Practice Functional and Spontaneous Communication

When speech training at home, it's important to start off by making sure your child is comfortable communicating their basic needs and wants without requiring any assistance. Avoid teaching your child any further skills before they have mastered this first step. If you notice your child's speech isn't adequate for functional conversations, you can practice different forms of Augmentative-Alternative Communication (AAC). A few examples of AAC exercises include voice-prompting devices, photo boards, cards, or sign language.

2. Give Your Child Plenty of Social Instruction

Children with ASD experience a difficult time understanding socially acceptable behavior. This could make them feel awkward interacting with others in social settings. You can teach your child certain social cues by providing them with clear and easy-to-follow instructions.

For example, you can teach your young child how to listen to a person when they are speaking, how to follow directions, and what kind of questions to ask in social settings. If you have older children, you can teach them how to express their ideas in group settings, or how to offer support to their friends. Some of the tools that can help you provide social instruction include visual reminders, reading books, or videos modeling acceptable social behavior.

3. Create Opportunities for Peer Interactions

Children with autism tend to feel overwhelmed by social interactions. Giving your child as much exposure to other children in play situations, can build their self-confidence and improve their peer relationships. Besides exposing your child to other children, you can also teach them how to play with others, take turns playing with toys, and respond when other children call your child's name.

Play Therapy

Play is an essential component of early childhood development. Young children learn how to socialize, communicate, and build their sense of self through play. Children with ASD love to play although they prefer to play alone, and their form of play is repetitive without any opportunity for exploration. This kind of isolated and repetitive play can cause children with ASD to become stuck in an unimaginative and unfulfilling pattern of play.

Play therapy was originally designed to be a type of psychotherapy offered to child survivors of abuse and trauma. It provided an outlet for these children to express their feelings in a safe and familiar environment. While play therapy is still used for trauma healing, it has also been found to assist children with ASD in building social and communication skills.

Similar to DIR, play therapy involves getting on your child's level and developing a strong relationship as you engage in the kind of activities and interests they enjoy. During playtime, your child learns valuable skills that can improve how they relate to others. For example, playing with a doll and pretending to comfort it can teach your child how to be less self-absorbed and focus on another person's emotional experience. They can explore possible emotions the doll is feeling, consider the various situations that could have contributed to their emotional state, and think of creative ways to calm the doll.

It is important to find a play therapist who your child is comfortable being around. Since they will be engaging with your child through play, it is important that both of them build a good rapport. You can also choose to do play therapy at home on your own. There are plenty of resources online that can guide you through the kind of skills you can teach your child through play.

Music Therapy

Music therapy involves using musical instruments or interactions to help those with cognitive or emotional challenges develop new skills. Musical therapists can help children with ASD lower their fear or anxiety of social interactions and improve their self-confidence. Since playing with music requires movement, music therapy can also increase your child's body awareness and coordination, and address any sensory issues.

Therapists have found that children on the spectrum tend to enjoy listening to music because of how soothing or engaging it can be. Therefore, music is often used as a tool to reinforce certain desirable behaviors in children or help them cope with sensory overload. If you have noticed your child responds favorably to music, you can look into music therapy as a strategy to teach your child certain skills.

Similar to other therapies, a musical therapist will start by assessing your child's needs and create a treatment plan with specific goals and objectives. The therapist may decide to work with your child on a one-on-one basis or invite them to join a group. In most cases, the treatment plan offered to your child will include interventions you can practice at home. Some of the activities on the treatment plan may include:

- Singing

- Dancing

- Listening to certain types of music

- Learning how to play an instrument

- Writing song lyrics

- Composing music

Music therapy is most effective when used alongside other therapies or interventions. It is rarely used as a primary intervention but can work well as a complementary strategy. If you are interested in trying out music therapy, look for a licensed musical therapist who is knowledgeable about brain development, the effect of music on well-being, musical instruments, and social ways to interact with music.

Exercise: Choosing the Right Therapies for Your Child

There are many different types of autism treatment options to choose from. However, not every option will be a good fit for your child. The best therapies are usually those that are aligned with the goals you and your child have. Whether you are researching new therapies on the market or thinking of switching to a different form of therapy, asking yourself certain questions can simplify your decision-making process.

List the therapies you are considering and for each one, answer the following questions:

- What are the benefits and drawbacks of this type of therapy?

- Does the therapy align with your child's developmental goals?

- Will you be required to take the lead or do you need to seek a therapist?

- Will this therapy be covered by your insurance provider? If not, are there any government programs that can assist in the costs?

You can also consider how much family involvement the therapy will require and whether it is something you can incorporate into your family's lifestyle. Remember, the aim of any therapy is to ensure your child learns life-long skills and becomes a better version of themselves. Therefore, the work your child does during therapy sessions should also extend to how they learn, play, and socialize in other aspects of their life.

Key Takeaways

It can be useful to dedicate your efforts to finding the right therapy for your child so you can manage their ASD symptoms and support them in their development. The role of therapy isn't to make your child with ASD look, sound, and act as closely to neurotypical children as possible, but instead to help them build self-confidence and learn skills that can improve their relationships with others. Even though each intervention is effective in its own right, some of them may not be a good fit for your child. Do your research, speak to your doctors, and find options that align with your goals.

It can take as much as 8—36 months to receive a diagnosis for ASD. This doesn't sound like a long time, but just think of how much a typical child develops in just 6 months, and now imagine the delays it can cause for the development of a child with autism. Since you cannot afford to wait, the next chapter is dedicated to interventions you can do at home.

Chapter 9:

What You Can Do for Your

Child at Home

In this chapter you will learn:

- How you can assist your child with autism at home, without having professional training.

Safety First

As a parent with a child on the spectrum, there is perhaps nothing more important to you than ensuring your child's safety. Whether it is at home or out in public, you are constantly thinking about ways to protect your child from perceived threats and overstimulation.

Your safety concerns are not just your own. They also impact your family and the kind of lifestyle you embrace. All family members share the burden of making sure the child with autism isn't triggered by stimuli or situations in their environment.

Even though 'safety' can look different for everyone, there are a few basic strategies you can implement at home to ensure your child with autism's safety. The strategies are presented below:

1. Create a Safety Plan

It can be easier to manage meltdowns or other unforeseen emergencies when you have a solid plan laid out. Your safety plan can include contact details of emergency medical staff and therapists, original diagnosis paperwork, your child's treatment plan, medication specifications, and a list of behaviors or stimuli that trigger your child (and how to calm them down when they are aroused). Update your safety plan as your child's treatment plan changes or when new behaviors or medical conditions emerge.

2. Teach Your Child Water Safety

Many children with autism have an affinity for water. Thus, swimming should be a basic skill your child learns from an early age. You can find swimming classes tailored for children with autism, led by a trained swimming coach. Before signing up, make sure the coach has worked with special needs children before and is comfortable with repetition and breaking down the process into small manageable steps.

3. Use Technological Devices as Safety Tools

There are various technological apps and devices on the market that can help you keep up with your growing child. For instance, you can install cameras or a home alarm system so you can easily find your child when they wander off. You can also download online games that teach your child safety skills, or have a built-in GPS function that lets you know your child's whereabouts throughout the day.

4. Create Safety Protocols for Emergencies

Create rules and protocols for your family to follow whenever you are confronted with an emergency, such as an unexpected fire. You can have a discussion about "safe places" around the home, a specific routine to follow in case of an emergency, people to contact, and so on. Once your plan is in place, have regular run-throughs so that your child isn't caught off guard during a real life-threatening situation.

5. Have a List of People Responsible for Your Child

There will be times when you have to go away and will be forced to leave your child with someone else. Think about the people you trust to take care of your child in your absence and notify each person of their duties and when you are most likely to call on them. If you have other older children, you can introduce a buddy system and assign an older child to take care of your child with ASD in public or for a few hours while you prepare dinner. You can also enlist the help of relatives, trusted neighbors, family friends, therapists, and school teachers.

The five strategies highlighted above can improve the safety of your home environment. However, there are also small adjustments you can make to your living arrangement that can make each area of the home child-friendly. Look at the tips below and consider how many you have already applied in your home:

- Keep medication and cleaning supplies out of reach

- Place pictures and labels on items around the home

- Set house rules and boundaries (i.e. Having "no go areas" or cabinets that cannot be opened)

- Install sensors and locks on cabinets, doors, and windows

- Place covers on all electric outlets

- Lock the water heater to ensure the water temperature doesn't get too hot

- Bind appliance wires and hide them in the wall or inside cabinets

The Safety Planning Cycle

Ensuring your child's safety isn't about telling them what to do or what not to do. Instead, it is about teaching them certain skills that prepare them for everyday life situations. The safety planning cycle, created by the Organization for Autism Research, provides a step-by-step approach to speaking about safety topics, addressing concerns, and creating safety protocols with your child. As your child grows older, each step in the safety planning cycle should be revised.

There are five steps that go as follows:

1. Understand

The first step is to introduce the safety topic to your child and think about the various factors that affect your child's safety. Ask yourself: What does my child need to know about this topic? Which key points are important to discuss at their developmental age?

2. Prepare

Next, think about the different kinds of resources that you can use to teach your child more about this particular safety topic. You might find that drawing a diagram, creating a mind map, reading a book, or watching age-appropriate safety videos can make it easier for your child to learn about the topic. Have all of your resources on hand when you are ready to address your safety concerns.

3. Practice

Your child with ASD may be able to understand the importance of the safety topics through the use of visual aids and other learning material. However, practice ensures they are confident in taking necessary action when the situation arises.

When practicing safety skills, break them down into small actionable steps and find ways to incorporate the steps into your child's daily routine. For example, if you are teaching your child to notify you before they wander off, incorporating dialogue, hand signals, or timers (timing how long your child is away) can be great ways to reinforce this safety concern in your child's daily routine.

4. Share

Your child's safety isn't your concern alone. Everybody who plays a role in your child's life should be aware of the safety skills and behaviors to practice around your child. When you have taught your child a new safety skill, let your child's therapists and educators know. You can also share advice on how others can support your child, like discussing common triggering behaviors to avoid when your child is around.

5. Update

When your child is old enough, you will be able to work together with them on creating a safety plan. They will be able to guide you on what safety practices feel comfortable for them, and new safety needs they might have. If your child isn't old enough to discuss their safety plan with you, consider consulting with your pediatrician or therapist on ways to make the safety plan more suitable to your child's needs.

Physical and Sexual Safety

Since your child with ASD may experience difficulty expressing themselves, teaching them various ways of protecting their bodies and speaking up about inappropriate forms of physical touch or abuse is extremely important. From the time your child is able to understand basic concepts about physical space and boundaries, you can teach them how to recognize when they are in threatening situations. Here are a few suggestions on how to educate your child on physical and sexual safety:

- Help your child identify trusted adults they can approach to talk about any issue they might have.

- Teach your child about their body parts using the correct names and discuss inappropriate forms of touch.

- Discuss what private parts are and who has access to see their private parts. You can also discuss exceptional circumstances when someone like a doctor might need to see their private parts.

- Teach your child the importance of boundaries and that it is okay to refuse to be hugged, kissed, or held by people they are not comfortable with. For instance, you can role-play situations where your child declines a hug from a relative or friend.

As a parent, it is important to learn the signs of physical abuse so you can intervene immediately. Common physical signs of abuse may include unexplained bruising, pain, weight loss, crying, or mood changes. You might also notice that your child's sleeping patterns have changed, they have become more emotionally withdrawn, or avoid being around certain people or situations.

You can also get into the habit of regularly asking your child questions about their time with caregivers. Abusers often target children who cannot or are afraid of saying 'no,' so you can look out for signs of grooming or that your child is feeling intimidated around certain caregivers. Lastly, ensure you hire caregivers who are trained in childcare, have obtained the necessary education or certification, and have been screened by healthcare facilities or schools. Always trust your gut instinct when choosing the right caregivers for your child and don't be afraid to speak up if you have any concerns.

How to Create Comfortable Routines

Routines are the foundation for early childhood development. They offer children enough structure and predictability in their day to assist in learning new skills. Children with autism require routines to reduce stress and anxiety and give them the confidence to make the most of their days. They can also make children with ASD more cooperative in daily tasks, minimize power struggles, and foster a healthy parent-child connection.

When your child knows what to expect, they are less anxious and can regulate their emotions better. This might also help them maintain focus on tasks for longer periods and be more open to participating in shared experiences with other people. You can create a routine for your child by following the C.A.L.M method below:

1. Create

The first step is to create a routine. You can do this by identifying daily tasks you would like your child to accomplish. When you have identified the daily tasks, you can organize them according to the order you would like them completed. This will give you the framework of your routine. You can choose how to design the routine in a creative way so that it can be understood by your child. Consider adding photos, color-coding tasks, and making it visually engaging.

2. Alert

A routine is of no use if it cannot be followed consistently. Set alerts on your phone to remind you whenever you need to switch between tasks. If you have an older child, give them a timer to use when completing individual tasks, such as homework. When the timer rings, it could signal switching to another task or taking a break. Have fun with your alerts by choosing quirky sounds to play whenever your child is about to complete a certain task. For instance, you might play a rooster noise to wake them up, and a cow noise when it is time to eat. Once you have assigned a specific sound to a task, avoid making any changes so your child can learn how to react to the sound and complete the task without being reminded.

3. Like

Show approval when your child completes their daily tasks. The more positive reinforcement you give, the more motivated they will be to continue making good progress. You can even use visual representations to show approval, like sticking an image of a thumbs up next to each completed task.

4. Maintain

Finally, remember consistency is key. Your aim should be to maintain the routine for as long as possible, without any major shifts or changes. It is normal for your child to resist the routine at the beginning or find it difficult to complete all daily tasks. Avoid lowering your expectations; instead, offer plenty of encouragement. Once your routine has been established, you can consider making adjustments or adding more tasks, such as scheduled play dates once a week.

A routine is only effective if it supports your child's development. Therefore, it is important to measure the success of the routine by monitoring your child's behavior and how well they are able to follow it. Consider each task on the routine to be a goal and track the following metrics:

- How many tasks your child completes a day.

- How many tasks your child completes without troublesome behavior.

- How many tasks your child completes without being reminded or assisted.

- How easily your child completes the entire daily routine.

If you are tech-savvy, you might be interested in digital tools that can help you plan your child's day. In recent years, autism apps have gained popularity and have become a great way to create and organize children's routines. Some of the main features of these apps include:

- Keeping track of remaining and completed tasks

- Sending alerts and reminders before tasks are set to begin

- Providing visual countdowns and timers

- Spoken text for children who are not yet able to read

- Helping your child remain focused on each task at hand

On rare occasions, you will need to make slight adjustments to your child's routine. You may be visiting friends or family, going on vacation, or going to a doctor's appointment. Completing tasks in a different order can be upsetting for your child with ASD whose condition makes them feel uncomfortable with change or transitions. However, since you will be able to plan for changes in advance, you can prepare your child for these upcoming changes and manage their expectations. Here are a few tips that can help you:

- **Create a social story and inform your child about the events that are going to take place.** Use language they can understand and end the story on a positive note. For example, "In three days we are going on an adventure to the land of groceries. We are going to buy juice, bread, and cheese! Then afterward, we are going to drive home and create a delicious sandwich together."

- **Notify your child about upcoming changes by writing them down on a timetable.** When your child looks at their timetable, they can see when certain events are going to happen. You can also add details, like what items your child will need to bring. For example, next to "Visit to the library" you can add "Bring your books" to ensure they are fully prepared for what will take place.

- **Give your child enough time to prepare for the new experiences.** Start speaking to your child about upcoming events days or weeks prior. When speaking to them, repeat the same stories and explain the process in the same way. On the day of the event, spend extra time alone with your child preparing them for what will happen. You can even do an hour-by-hour countdown to make the event feel less daunting.

On extremely rare occasions, you will be confronted with changes that you can't prepare for ahead of time. These changes may come in the form of emergencies or situations that are out of your control. One way to prepare your child for these unexpected changes is to introduce a question mark on your visual cards if you use a visual schedule for daily activities. Think of this as the "wild card" that represents mystery.

For example, if you are going outdoors on an outing, you can slip in a question mark card or write down a question mark on your child's timetable. Prepare an enjoyable activity so that your child associates the question mark with pleasurable experiences. You can also add a question mark during at-home activities or when visiting social scenes that could make your child feel anxious, like birthday parties.

Remember to prepare a fun activity each time the question mark is presented. Eventually, you can add the question mark whenever your child is going to perform an activity they dislike, such as visiting the dentist. Immediately after the experience, reward your child with an enjoyable experience and go back to their predictable routine. When your child is comfortable seeing the question mark and has neutral or positive feelings about it, you can use it whenever you are faced with unexpected changes.

Incorporating Different Types of Play

Play is essential for all growing children, but for children with autism, in particular, it can be a great way to practice and reinforce new skills and abilities. Play isn't just about picking up different toys, but also about exploring the environment, sharing experiences, problem-solving, and being imaginative.

There are different types of play you can practice at home to help your child develop certain skills. Here are six types of play to consider:

1. Exploratory Play

Exploratory play involves teaching your child how to explore a variety of objects, rather than playing with only a few. You can also teach them to use toys creatively, such as pretending a stuffed animal is a real baby or building a castle out of building blocks. Exploratory play is about helping your child feel comfortable exploring the world around them through embracing different objects.

2. Cause-and-Effect Play

Cause-and-effect play involves introducing your child to toys that require their active involvement, like pushing a button in order for the computer to speak. These kinds of activities can teach your child that their actions carry specific results. Once they become aware of this, they can trigger certain results by taking different actions. This type of play can help your child develop confidence in making decisions and trusting their own judgment.

3. Toy Play

Toy play is the most common type of play. All it requires is teaching your child how to play with toys according to their original purpose. For example, toy cars were intended to be pushed on a carpet and building blocks were intended to be stacked on top of each other. Toy play can help your child learn to solve problems creatively and feel comfortable taking the lead. It can also help them learn how to play with common toys in social settings.

4. Constructive Play

Constructive play is about taking a number of different objects and forming a new object or creation. It teaches your child how to set goals, imagine the end results, and work toward achieving something. This is also another fun way of teaching your child how to problem-solve or practice delayed gratification: Sorting different puzzle pieces might not be fun in the beginning, but seeing the final picture in its fullness is extremely satisfying.

5. Physical Play

Physical play requires movement. It could involve your child going through an obstacle course, rough-and-tumbling with you on the floor, or kicking a ball outside. Your child can benefit from this type of play because it encourages them to stretch their body, improve their motor skills, and get comfortable being in close contact with trusted people.

6. Pretend Play

Pretend play, or role-playing, happens when your child uses their imagination to see the world differently. As a parent, this type of play can be a great way to teach your child social behaviors or language that can improve their peer relationships. Pretend play can also help your child develop empathy, by allowing them to imagine other people's experiences and what they may be thinking or feeling. The best way to practice pretend play is to model typical scenarios your child witnesses on a daily basis, like watching you prepare a meal. Remember to make it fun by pulling different facial expressions, wearing quirky costumes, or using silly accents.

Once your child is comfortable playing at home, you can encourage them to play in different environments, like at the local park or when you visit a family member. It is also important to notice when your child isn't in the mood to play. In these situations, you can provide them with stimulation by reading a book in a relaxing tone of voice or allowing them to watch an educational program on TV. When your child loses interest in an activity, let them guide you on the next activity they would like to focus on.

And if you are ever short on ideas of what fun and educational games or exercises you can play, simply refer to the list below:

- Give your child a bottle of bubbles to teach them self-control

- Play musical statues to develop your child's motor skills

- Play interactive games, like Jenga, to teach your child creative problem-solving

- Teach your child how to play Scrabble so they can learn planning and organization skills (it can also be a great memory-building game)

- Role-play with puppets, tea sets, or playing dress up

- Play sorting games to increase your child's vocabulary (this might include sorting the laundry or groceries, etc.)

- Make flashcards with different vocabulary. Then, cut a hole in a shoebox and ask your child to drop different words inside

- Take turns coloring a picture, singing song lyrics, adding ingredients to a recipe, or practicing dance moves

- Create shopping lists together (these do not need to be written, they can be visual lists too)

- Play with building blocks to teach your child how to follow instructions and sequencing

Get in Tune With Your Child's Senses

In Chapter 5, we discussed how sensory overload can contribute to autism meltdowns, and common symptoms of hyperarousal, such as self-regulatory behaviors, also known as stimming. It is impossible to prevent sensory overload from taking place due to the manner in which your child's brain processes information. However, you can become an expert when it comes to your child's sensory triggers and do your best to keep them at bay.

Here are some general sensory triggers that many children with autism may experience:

- **Touch triggers:** Wearing clothes made with rough or scratchy fabric, eating food while it is still hot, being picked up by a stranger or handled in a rough manner, or getting in a bathtub with very hot water.

- **Visual triggers:** Entering a room with bright lights, seeing flashing cameras on a TV screen, shopping in a crowded store, or visiting a place, like a museum or amusement park, where there is a lot of commotion.

- **Auditory triggers:** Hearing loud noises, being surprised with a sudden bang, overhearing people shouting at each other, or listening to different sounds playing at the same time (i.e. Trying to watch a cartoon show while there are adults talking in the background).

- **Smell triggers:** Smelling pungent perfume or foods, noticing subtle smells that others may not notice, or refusing to enter certain rooms due to the disturbing smell.

- **Taste triggers:** Certain flavors might be overwhelming for your child, such as spicy, salty, or sweet foods. A combination of different flavors on a plate might also be triggering.

Becoming an expert on your child's sensory triggers is one way of helping them self-regulate. However, there are some triggers that cannot be avoided, especially when they are related to water, the touch of a toilet seat, and all red foods, for example. In the long run, it is better to teach your child how to manage sensory overload and regulate their own emotions when feeling triggered. This will help your child feel less anxious when they become hyper-aroused, particularly when you are not around. Here are a few strategies to help you teach your child how to manage sensory overload:

- **Teach your child age-appropriate self-soothing techniques.** You can teach your child to practice calming techniques like breathing, stretching their body, or taking a moment for themselves when they are feeling stressed. These self-soothing techniques can calm their nervous system and reduce reactive behavior.

- **Introduce self-soothing toys for a positive distraction.** When your child starts going to school, you might want to put a self-soothing toy in their school bag, so they can play with the toy whenever they are feeling stressed. The self-soothing toy is also great for them to play with in social settings with a lot of sensory stimuli, like at a kid's birthday party or shopping mall.

- **Teach your child an exit strategy when they are feeling triggered.** As part of safety planning, you can teach your child a simple process to follow when they find themselves triggered. This might involve going into a quiet room and taking a few deep breaths, approaching a teacher and expressing their discomfort, or retreating to their bedroom and playing with their self-soothing toy.

- **Incorporate physical exercise in your child's routine.** Physical exercise is a great way to keep your child active, healthy, and burn a lot of energy. Regular exercise can manage stress, regulate moods, and help your child sleep better at night.

- **Dress your child in a weighted vest or wrap a blanket around their chest.** Sometimes, all it takes for your child to regulate their body is feeling a sense of security. When they are wearing a weighted vest or wrapped in a blanket, it can feel as pleasurable as a warm embrace.

- **Make time for playing with pets.** If you have a pet in the family, ensure your child gets some time playing with it. If not, a visit to the local park can be a great way to meet and pet a few furry animals. The reason animal therapy is so effective is that animals have a calming effect on human beings, including children. Playing and caring for animals can also help your child cultivate empathy and regulate their emotions better.

The Best Diet for Your Child

Every growing child can benefit from consuming a healthy and balanced diet. However, for children with autism, some foods that are generally considered 'healthy' may cause digestive or eating-related issues. Nevertheless, since children with autism are prone to nutrient deficits, it is important to ensure your child receives the right amount of vitamins and minerals while avoiding foods that may cause disturbances.

Besides getting the right amount of nutrients, parents may struggle to get their children to eat certain foods. This is mostly due to feeding issues and ritualistic eating habits that many children on the spectrum have. For example, a child who doesn't enjoy the texture of a certain food might spit the food out or lump the food in their cheeks, rather than eat it. Or in other cases, the color, texture, or smell of a food can make a child refuse to eat it.

If you notice that your child has digestive or feeding issues, consult with your pediatrician and nutritionist so they can put together an eating plan that works for your child. Cutting out certain foods just because your child refuses to eat them won't work out in the long run. The better approach would be to slowly work on changing your child's eating habits and encouraging them to be more tolerant of unwanted foods.

As a way to integrate healthy foods into your child's diet, your doctor or nutritionist might recommend trying out one of the three most common diets for children with autism, which are:

- **Autism MEAL plan:** This diet isn't solely focused on incorporating as many nutritious foods in your child's diet. It emphasizes the importance of healthy eating behaviors and changing your child's attitude toward certain foods.

- **Gluten-free/Casein-free diet (GFCF):** The GFCF diet can relieve common digestive issues a child with autism may experience. This is after studies found that both gluten and dairy products can worsen digestion problems in autistic people. However, it is still important to find great gluten and dairy substitutes so your child gets sufficient protein, amino acids, and whole grains in their diet.

- **Modified ketogenic diet:** Children with autism can benefit from a low carb, moderate protein, and high-fat diet. It can help them avoid gluten products found in many processed carb foods and add more lean proteins and healthy fats that are great for muscle growth and strengthening, heart health, and brain development.

Studies have also found that due to food preferences and intolerances, children with autism are often deficient in the following nutrients:

- Fiber

- Folic acid

- Calcium

- Iron

- Zinc

- Vitamins A, C, D, E, K, B6, and B12

To ensure your child gets enough of the above nutrients, try incorporating the following foods in their diet, with the help of a nutritionist:

- Beans (like black beans, pinto beans, or navy beans)

- Nuts (especially peanuts and peanut butter)

- Seeds (like sunflower seeds or chia seeds)

- Eggs

- Seafood

- Lean beef, turkey, or chicken

- Alternative types of milk (like soy or almond milk)

- Dried fruits

- Fresh fruits (citrus, melons, tomatoes, or berries)

- Onion and garlic

- Pumpkin and butternut squash

- Cruciferous vegetables

- Fortified breakfast cereals

Exercise: Detecting Different Levels of Threat

The following scale was created by the Organization for Autism Research. It is an activity that you can complete with your child when discussing threat levels around strangers or people your child may not be comfortable around. For example, it can help your child understand that not all strangers are bad. There are some strangers who might be somewhat familiar and make them feel excited, but there are also other strangers who they may not know very well who make them feel scared.

The threat detection scale consists of five levels of threat, level five being the most concerning. In other words, when your child rates a threat as being a level five, they are typically in danger (whether real or imagined), and should reach out to the nearest caregiver. This scale can be a great safety topic to discuss with your child on a regular basis, to ensure they know how to react around threatening people.

Below is an example of a completed scale:

Rating	Looks like...	Feels like...	What should I do?
5	Someone I haven't met before is asking me to go somewhere with them	Scary and stressful	Say no and walk away quickly. If I cannot walk away, then I can yell for help
4	Someone I haven't met before is trying to talk to me	Overwhelming and intimidating	Find mom and dad (or a trusted caregiver) and tell that what happened
3	Someone who looks or	Confused, but curious	Approach mom and dad

Rating	Looks like...	Feels like...	What should I do?
	sounds familiar, but can't remember their name		first (or a trusted caregiver) and ask if it is safe to talk to them
2	Teacher, doctor, or therapist	Relaxed and excited	Make sure mom and dad know where I am and who I am with
1	Aunt, uncle, or other close relative	Calm and comfortable	Stay close to them and inform them before wandering somewhere

Now it is your turn to fill out your own scale based on safety concerns specific to your child:

Rating	Looks like...	Feels like...	What should I do?
5			
4			
3			

Rating	Looks like...	Feels like...	What should I do?
2			
1			

Key Takeaways

There are lots of ways that parents, caregivers, siblings, aunts, uncles, and grandparents can help children with autism and they don't need any professional training or to spend a fortune on educational toys, or hours at a time. It only takes five minutes a day to help your child: Five minutes of quality time with no interruptions. None of the strategies in this chapter will harm your child in any way, so you are welcome to start implementing them as soon as you are suspicious of any developmental issues.

Conclusion

ASD is a developmental disorder that affects parts of the brain, particularly those related to the development of the nervous system, behavior, and communication. Adults are often diagnosed with ASD when they are still children, from as early as 12 months. However, if symptoms are subtle, the condition may only be picked up later on in the child's development, like when they start attending school.

The reason early detection is so important is that ASD doesn't have a known cure. After receiving a diagnosis, doctors will often place a child on a treatment plan to manage ASD-related symptoms that interfere with their early childhood development, such as learning social, language, and communication skills.

It is true that when you meet one person with autism, you have met one person with autism. Since autism exists on a spectrum, how it affects one child's development may be different from how it appears in another child. Therefore, instead of memorizing fixed symptoms, doctors rely on the criteria laid out in the DSM-5 to identify a variety of autism symptoms.

Without being knowledgeable about this condition, it can be easy for parents to misinterpret their child's behavior as being defiant. How else can they explain the lengthy meltdowns, refusal to eat certain foods, and not being interested to engage with friends and family members? However, what might appear as a naughty child may very well be an overstimulated child who feels unsettled by the loud noises, unfamiliar faces, and really strong smell coming from the kitchen.

Learning how to parent a child with autism requires a willingness to learn from your child, and at times, allow them to signal what they need. You may not understand your child's triggers, like not following a consistent routine, but when you start paying attention to their behaviors, you will learn the cause of their emotional outbursts and better ways to approach tasks.

Your child has a unique way of processing information and responding to the world around them. Take the time to learn how they think, what excites them, and what their strengths are. Let their individuality inspire you to raise them according to their needs and not how society expects them to live. You have the freedom to rewrite the rules of what it means to parent a child with social and learning disabilities and offer your child the most enriching childhood possible.

Don't forget the importance of play, storytelling, and visual representations because this is how children learn best. Furthermore, be consistent in your routines and techniques and let everyone involved in your child's life know the safety plan.

Remember to take care of yourself and find ways of managing stress in your own life. Happy parents create the safest home environment for your growing child, so carve out time for yourself and don't hesitate to reach out to your support system for help.

ASD is not a disease; therefore, it doesn't need a cure. All it requires is a team of supportive people who can help you provide your child with the skills and confidence they need to become the best version of themselves. Reach out to your nearest medical doctors, therapists, and special needs educators for reassurance and emotional support on this journey of parenting your child with autism.

Finally, learn how to stop and cherish the small moments where you get to bond with your child. It may not look like the typical connection you experience with your other children, but it doesn't need to. Communication doesn't occur with words alone. It can happen with the touch of a hand, showing you a heart flashcard, or a few seconds of eye contact.

These may all be subtle ways your child chooses to reaffirm their love for you and show you just how much they appreciate your support.

About the Author

Richard Bass is a well-established author with extensive knowledge and background on children's disabilities. Richard has also experienced first-hand many children and teens who deal with depression and anxiety. He enjoys researching techniques and ideas to better serve students, as well as providing guidance to parents on how to understand and lead their children to success.

Richard Bass holds a bachelor's and master's degree in education as well as several certifications including Special Education K-12, and Educational Administration.

He wants to share his experience, research, and practices through his writing as it has proven successful to many parents and students.

Richard feels there is a need for parents and others around the child to fully understand the disability. He hopes that with his writing, readers will be more understanding of children with disabilities.

Whenever Richard is not working, reading, or writing, he likes to travel with his family to learn about different cultures as well as get ideas from all around the world about the upbringing of children, especially those with disabilities. Richard also researches and learns about different educational systems around the world.

Richard participates in several online groups where parents, educators, doctors, and psychologists share their success with children with disabilities. He plans to form a group where further discussion about his books and techniques could take place. Apart from online groups, he has also attended training regarding the upbringing of students with disabilities and has also led training in this area.

Richard has published three other books apart from this one including *A Beginner's Guide on Parenting Children with ADHD* , *Parenting Children with Oppositional Defiant Disorder* and *Overcoming Anxiety and Depression in Teens.*

A Message From the Author

If you enjoyed the book and are interested in further updates or just a place to share your thoughts with other readers or me, please join my Facebook group by scanning below!

If you would be interested in receiving a FREE Planner for kids (PDF version), by signing up you will also receive exclusive notifications when new content is released and will be able to receive it at a promotional price. Scan below to sign up!

If you are interested on learning more about Neuro-development check out my YouTube channel by clicking below!

References

Ada's Medical Knowledge Team. (2017). Signs of autism. Ada.com; Ada. https://ada.com/signs-of-autism/

Applied Behavior Analysis Programs. (n.d.). 5 Types of behavior therapy for individuals with autism. Applied Behavior Analysis Programs Guide. https://www.appliedbehavioranalysisprograms.com/lists/5-types-of-behavior-therapy-for-individuals-with-autism/#:~:text=One%20type%20of%20behavior%20therapy

AppliedBehaviorAnalysisEdu. (2017). 4 Ways a child with autism processes information differently. Appliedbehavioranalysisedu.org. https://www.appliedbehavioranalysisedu.org/4-ways-a-child-with-autism-processes-information-differently/

Autism Speaks. (2013). Study finds sensory integration therapy benefits children with autism. Autism Speaks. https://www.autismspeaks.org/science-news/study-finds-sensory-integration-therapy-benefits-children-autism

Autism Speaks. (2019a). Medical conditions associated with autism. Autism Speaks. https://www.autismspeaks.org/medical-conditions-associated-autism

Autism Speaks. (2019b). Medicines for treating autism's core symptoms. Autism Speaks.

https://www.autismspeaks.org/medicines-treating-autisms-core-symptoms

Autism Speaks. (2019c). Relationship Development Intervention (RDI). Autism Speaks. https://www.autismspeaks.org/relationship-development-intervention-rdi-0

Autism Speaks. (2021). Applied Behavior Analysis (ABA). Autism Speaks. https://www.autismspeaks.org/applied-behavior-analysis

Barloso, K. (2021, May 7). Managing autism meltdowns, tantrums and aggression. Autism Parenting Magazine. https://www.autismparentingmagazine.com/autism-meltdowns/

Better Perlis, L., & ADDitude Editors. (2022, April 11). ADHD, anxiety, and autism: Your AAA guidebook. ADDitude. https://www.additudemag.com/slideshows/adhd-anxiety-and-autism-symptoms-and-treatment/

Breit, S., Kupferberg, A., Rogler, G., & Hasler, G. (2018). Vagus nerve as modulator of the brain–gut axis in psychiatric and inflammatory disorders. Frontiers in Psychiatry, 9(44). https://doi.org/10.3389/fpsyt.2018.00044

Burch, K. (2022, February 11). Baby milestone: Walking. *BabyCenter.* https://www.babycenter.com/baby/baby-development/baby-milestone-walking_6507

Çakmak, K. (2021, December 4). Sensory overload in autism: Sensitivity differences. Otsimo. https://otsimo.com/en/sensory-overload-autism/

Centers for Disease Control and Prevention. (2020, March 25). What is Autism Spectrum Disorder? Centers for Disease Control and Prevention; CDC. https://www.cdc.gov/ncbddd/autism/facts.html

Cerny, B. (2021, September). 5 Key principles of the TEACCH method. Applied Behavior Analysis Programs Guide. https://www.appliedbehavioranalysisprograms.com/lists/key-principles-of-the-teacch-method/

Cherry, K. (2021, January 13). What developmental milestones do children experience? Verywell Family. https://www.verywellfamily.com/what-is-a-developmental-milestone-2795123

Clark, C. (2015, September 6). 5 Principles of speech therapy for children with autism. Speech and Language Kids. https://www.speechandlanguagekids.com/5-principles-of-speech-therapy-autism/

Davis, C. P. (2021, April 5). Types of autism medications and treatments. MedicineNet; MedicineNet. https://www.medicinenet.com/types_of_autism_medications_and_treatments/drug-class.htm

de Fina, C., & Anderson, A. (2017, July 7). Play and children with autism spectrum disorder. Raising Children Network. https://raisingchildren.net.au/autism/school-play-work/play-learning/play-asd

Discovery Building Sets. (n.d.). What are social skills? And why are social skills important? Discovery Building Sets. https://discoverybuildingsets.com/blogs/dbs-articles/what-are-social-skills

Ebert, J. (2018, January 8). Social skills - The building blocks for life. The Potential Ability Group. https://potentialabilitygroup.com.au/social-skills-the-building-blocks-for-life/

Eckerd, M. (2014, August 7). Social skills building blocks. Smart Kids with Learning Disabilities. https://www.smartkidswithld.org/getting-help/making-friends/6-building-blocks-of-social-competency/#:~:text=Being%20assertive%2C%20listening%20well%2C%20compromising

Egber, M. (2021, April 6). 30 Quotes from 30 people with autism. Els for Autism. https://www.elsforautism.org/30-quotes-from-30-people-with-autism/

Elemy. (2020a, May 28). Relationship Development Intervention (RDI): How effective is it? The Elemy Learning Studio. https://www.elemy.com/studio/autism-treatment/relationship-development-intervention/

Elemy. (2020b, June 8). Do people with autism have "normal" empathy and emotions? The Elemy Learning Studio. https://www.elemy.com/studio/autism/empathy-and-emotions/

Elemy. (2020c, June 11). Strategies to handle autism meltdowns like an expert. The Elemy Learning Studio. https://www.elemy.com/studio/autism-symptoms/meltdowns/

Elemy. (2020d, June 18). The optimal food list for autism (and what to avoid). The Elemy Learning Studio.

https://www.elemy.com/studio/autism-and-diet/food-list/

firespringInt. (2019). 7 Disorders closely related to autism. Autism Research Institute. https://www.autism.org/related-disorders/

Goally. (2020, December 28). How to create routines for a child with autism. Goally. https://getgoally.com/blog/how-to-create-routines-for-a-child-with-autism/

Gwen. (2018, July 17). 18 Social skills activities for kids with autism and sensory issues. Meraki Lane. https://www.merakilane.com/18-social-skills-activities-for-kids-with-autism-and-sensory-issues/

Ha, S., Sohn, I.-J., Kim, N., Sim, H. J., & Cheon, K.-A. (2015). Characteristics of brains in Autism Spectrum Disorder: Structure, function and connectivity across the lifespan. Experimental Neurobiology, 24(4), 273. https://doi.org/10.5607/en.2015.24.4.273

Hatch-Rasmussen, C. (2019). Sensory integration in Autism Spectrum Disorders. Autism Research Institute. https://www.autism.org/sensory-integration/

Hess, P. (2020, May 8). Autistic girls may experience more emotional challenges than autistic boys do. Spectrum News. https://www.spectrumnews.org/news/autistic-girls-may-experience-more-emotional-challenges-than-autistic-boys-do/

Horeis, M. (2020, June 23). The vagus nerve: Your secret weapon in fighting stress. Www.allied-Services.org.

https://www.allied-services.org/news/2020/june/the-vagus-nerve-your-secret-weapon-in-fighting-s/

Hu, X., Han, Z. R., Bai, L., & Gao, M. M. (2019). The mediating role of parenting stress in the relations between parental emotion regulation and parenting behaviors in Chinese families of children with Autism Spectrum Disorders: A dyadic analysis. Journal of Autism and Developmental Disorders, 49(10), 3983–3998. https://doi.org/10.1007/s10803-019-04103-z

Integrity Inc. (n.d.). What are the 5 types of autism? Integrity Inc. https://www.integrityinc.org/what-are-the-5-types-of-autism/

Ivy Rehab. (2022, January 2). Sensory overload - Tips for helping sensory sensitive kids. Ivy Rehab. https://www.ivyrehab.com/news/sensory-overload-tips-for-helping-sensory-sensitive-kids/

Jin, Y., & Kong, J. (2017). Transcutaneous vagus nerve stimulation: A promising method for treatment of Autism Spectrum Disorders. Frontiers in Neuroscience, 10. https://doi.org/10.3389/fnins.2016.00609

Kid Sense Child Development. (2011). Play and social skills development checklist. Kid Sense Child Development. https://childdevelopment.com.au/resources/child-development-charts/play-and-social-skills-developmental-checklist/

Koscinski, C. (2019, May 4). What is sensory integration therapy and could it help your child? Harkla; Harkla. https://harkla.co/blogs/special-needs/sensory-integration-therapy

Lisi, E. (2020). What it's really like to have autism. In YouTube. https://www.youtube.com/watch?v=y4vurv9usYA

LuxAI. (2020, November 24). How to improve emotion recognition and understanding in children with autism. LuxAI S.A. https://luxai.com/blog/how-to-improve-emotion-recognition-and-understanding-in-children-with-autism/

LuxAI. (2021, March 17). How to teach emotion recognition and labelling to children with autism. LuxAI S.A. https://luxai.com/blog/emotion-recognition-for-autism/#activities

M, S. (2021, November 30). What are the 5 different types of autism? Diagnosis, treatment. MedicineNet. https://www.medicinenet.com/what_are_the_5_different_types_of_autism/article.htm

Mandavilli, A. (2015, October 19). The lost girls. Spectrum | Autism Research News. https://www.spectrumnews.org/features/deep-dive/the-lost-girls/

Marcus Autism Center. (n.d.). Early signs of autism. Marcus Autism Center. https://www.marcus.org/autism-resources/autism-tips-and-resources/early-signs-of-autism

McCarthy, L. F. (2022, March 30). ADHD Medications for children. ADDitude; ADDitude. https://www.additudemag.com/adhd-medications-for-children/

Miller, L. (2020, October 25). Why do autistic kids stim? And strategies to help. NatureDoc.

https://www.naturedoc.co.uk/why-do-autistic-kids-
stim-strategies-to-help/

Morin, A. (n.d.). Difference between ADHD and autism.
Www.understood.org.
https://www.understood.org/en/articles/the-
difference-between-adhd-and-autism

National Autistic Society. (2020, August 14). Meltdowns - A
guide   for   all   audiences.   Www.autism.org.uk.
https://www.autism.org.uk/advice-and-
guidance/topics/behaviour/meltdowns/all-audiences

Ohwovoriole, T. (2021, October 18). What causes autism?
Verywell   Mind.
https://www.verywellmind.com/autism-causes-and-
risk-factors-5195311

One Central Health. (2020, October 30). 10 Myths about
Autism Spectrum Disorder. One Central Health.
https://www.onecentralhealth.com.au/autism/10-
myths-about-autism/

Online Psychology at Pepperdine. (2018, December 3). How to
improve emotional self-regulation among children with
autism   and   attention   disorders.
Onlinegrad.pepperdine.edu.
https://onlinegrad.pepperdine.edu/blog/emotional-
self-regulation-children-autism/

Organization for Autism Research. (2016, March). Life journey
through autism: A guide to safety. Research Autism.
https://researchautism.org/wp-
content/uploads/2016/03/A_Guide_to_Safety.pdf

Pelini, S. (2018, January 17). An age-by-age guide to helping kids manage emotions. The Gottman Institute. https://www.gottman.com/blog/age-age-guide-helping-kids-manage-emotions/

Pietro, S. (2016, October 31). How can we help kids with self-regulation? Child Mind Institute; Child Mind Institute. https://childmind.org/article/can-help-kids-self-regulation/

Poquérusse, J., Pastore, L., Dellantonio, S., & Esposito, G. (2018). Alexithymia and Autism Spectrum Disorder: A complex relationship. Frontiers in Psychology, 9. https://doi.org/10.3389/fpsyg.2018.01196

Raising Children. (2020, November 18). Changing routines: Children and teenagers with autism spectrum disorder. Raising Children Network. https://raisingchildren.net.au/autism/behaviour/understanding-behaviour/changing-routines-asd

Raising Children. (2021, May 24). Treatment and Education of Autistic and related Communications Handicapped Children (TEACCH). Raising Children Network. https://raisingchildren.net.au/autism/therapies-guide/teacch#:~:text=The%20TEACCH%20program%20is%20based

Raising Children Network. (2020, December 7). Emotional development in children with autism spectrum disorder. Raising Children Network. https://raisingchildren.net.au/autism/development/social-emotional-development/emotional-development-asd

Rowden, A. (2021, March 5). What are the types of autism? Www.medicalnewstoday.com. https://www.medicalnewstoday.com/articles/types-of-autism#diagnosis-and-levels

Rudy, L. J. (2019, December 2). Music therapy for child with autismren. Verywell Health; Verywellhealth. https://www.verywellhealth.com/music-therapy-for-autism-260057

Rudy, L. J. (2021a, September 11). Why your child with autism will benefit from seeing a speech therapist. Verywell Health. https://www.verywellhealth.com/speech-therapy-for-autism-the-basics-260577

Rudy, L. J. (2021b, November 13). Who should evaluate your child for a possible autism diagnosis? Verywell Health. https://www.verywellhealth.com/who-should-diagnose-autism-spectrum-disorders-260333

Rudy, L. J. (2022a, February 28). 20 Ways to help a child with autism to stay calm or manage meltdowns. Verywell Health. https://www.verywellhealth.com/how-to-calm-a-child-with-autism-4177696

Rudy, L. J. (2022b, April 15). How can play therapy benefit your child with autism? Verywell Health. https://www.verywellhealth.com/play-therapy-and-autism-the-basics-260059

Salvatore, K. (n.d.). 5 Ways to help reduce anxiety in children with autism. Stages Learning. https://blog.stageslearning.com/blog/5-ways-help-reduce-anxiety-children-with-autism

Sarris, M. (2014, January 23). ADHD, anxiety and autism? Interactive Autism Network. https://iancommunity.org/ssc/autism-plus-another-diagnosis

Schaaf, R. C., Benevides, T., Mailloux, Z., Faller, P., Hunt, J., van Hooydonk, E., Freeman, R., Leiby, B., Sendecki, J., & Kelly, D. (2013). An intervention for sensory difficulties in children with autism: A randomized trial. Journal of Autism and Developmental Disorders, 44. https://doi.org/10.1007/s10803-013-1983-8

Schenkman, L. (2020, May 1). Autistic children's emotional problems may persist into young adulthood. Spectrum News. https://www.spectrumnews.org/news/autistic-childrens-emotional-problems-may-persist-into-young-adulthood/

Shah, P., Hall, R., Catmur, C., & Bird, G. (2016). Alexithymia, not autism, is associated with impaired interoception. Cortex, 81, 215–220. https://doi.org/10.1016/j.cortex.2016.03.021

Smith, K. (2016). Coping with stress while caring for a child with autism. Psycom.net. https://www.psycom.net/coping-with-stress-while-caring-for-a-child-with-autism/

Smith, M., & Segal, J. (2019, February 13). ADHD parenting tips. HelpGuide.org. https://www.helpguide.org/articles/add-adhd/when-your-child-has-attention-deficit-disorder-adhd.htm

Sole-Smith, V. (2014, February 24). The history of autism. Parents; Parents.

https://www.parents.com/health/autism/the-history-of-autism/

The Center for Autism Research. (2020, June 9). Diagnostic criteria for Autism Spectrum Disorder in the DSM-5. CAR Autism Roadmap. https://www.carautismroadmap.org/diagnostic-criteria-for-autism-spectrum-disorder-in-the-dsm5/

The Spectrum. (n.d.-a). Autism communication strategies that work. The Spectrum. https://thespectrum.org.au/autism-strategy/autism-strategy-communication/

The Spectrum. (n.d.-b). Support professionals for people with autism. The Spectrum. https://thespectrum.org.au/autism-support-services/professionals/

TherapistAid. (n.d.). Mindfulness activities for children (worksheet). Therapist Aid. https://www.therapistaid.com/therapy-worksheet/mindfulness-for-children/anxiety/children

Thompson, D. (2013, September 5). Double Diagnosis: When Your Child Has ADHD and Autism. Everyday Health. https://www.everydayhealth.com/add-adhd/double-diagnosis-when-your-child-has-adhd-and-autism.aspx

Trehub, S. E., Ghazban, N., & Corbeil, M. (2015). Musical affect regulation in infancy. Annals of the New York Academy of Sciences, 1337(1), 186–192. https://doi.org/10.1111/nyas.12622

Walkup, J. T. (n.d.). Best anxiety medications for children. Child Mind Institute.

https://childmind.org/article/best-medications-for-kids-anxiety/

Zeliadt, N. (2019, February 13). Nerves that control heart rate may contribute to autism. Spectrum News. https://www.spectrumnews.org/news/nerves-control-heart-rate-may-contribute-autism/

Image References

Dummer, A. (2019). Photo of toddler smiling [Online image]. In Pexels. https://www.pexels.com/photo/photo-of-toddler-smiling-1912868/

Fring, G. (2020). Small kid listening to music via headphones [Online image]. In Pexels. https://www.pexels.com/photo/small-kid-listening-to-music-via-headphones-4017437/

Gambardella, J. (2020). A child crying while playing with his brother [Online image]. In Pexels. https://www.pexels.com/photo/a-child-crying-while-playing-with-his-brother-6222764/

Krukov, Y. (n.d.). Little boy in white long sleeve crew neck shirt playing ukulele [Online image]. In Pexels. https://www.pexels.com/photo/little-boy-in-white-long-sleeve-crew-neck-shirt-playing-ukulele-8190037/

McCutcheon, S. (2018a). A kId with multicolored hand paint [Online image]. In Pexels. https://www.pexels.com/photo/a-kid-with-multicolored-hand-paint-1148998/

McCutcheon, S. (2018b). Person making clay figures [Online image]. In Pexels. https://www.pexels.com/photo/person-making-clay-figures-1449934/

Nilov, M. (2021). A little girl coloring with her grandparents [Online image]. In Pexels. https://www.pexels.com/photo/a-little-girl-coloring-with-her-grandparents-8307604/

Polesie Toys. (2016). A boy in striped shirt playing with a plastic toy animal [Online image]. In Pexels. https://www.pexels.com/photo/a-boy-in-striped-shirt-playing-with-a-plastic-toy-animal-6139573/

Polesie Toys. (2019). Girl in white tank top sitting on chair [Online image]. In Pexels. https://www.pexels.com/photo/love-people-woman-girl-4487869/

Polesie Toys. (2020). Girl in floral long sleeve shirt holding white plastic toy [Online image]. In Pexels. https://www.pexels.com/photo/girl-in-floral-long-sleeve-shirt-holding-white-plastic-toy-4484794/

Sharefaith. (n.d.). Boy wearing orange shirt blowing on dandelion [Online image]. In Pexels. https://www.pexels.com/photo/boy-wearing-orange-shirt-blowing-on-dandelion-1231215/

Printed in Great Britain
by Amazon

22204279R00108